DANG,
I WISH I HADN'T DONE THAT
AND OTHER SENIOR MOMENTS FROM THE
AGELESS AUTHORS WRITING CONTEST

Book 2
Compiled from
2018 Contest Results

Edited by
Larry Upshaw

DANG,
I Wish I Hadn't Done That

Published by
Ageless Authors
10844 Meadowcliff Lane
Dallas, Texas 75238

214.405.5093

info@agelessauthors.com

agelessauthors.com

Copies of this book may be purchased at the website,
agelessauthors.com, from Amazon.com and from many other
retail book outlets. If you should have any problem purchasing
from the website or anywhere else, please contact
Larry Upshaw by email:
publishing@agelessauthors.com.

ISBN: 978-0-578-56365-7

"It's none of their business
that you have to learn to write.
Let them think you were born that way."
—Ernest Hemingway

"Once I married a woman who asked if I was working today or just writing. She is what you call an ex-wife."

—Larry Upshaw

Table of Contents

Introduction		1
Military Memories		**5**
Refugee *First Prize*	Leah Lake Austin, Texas	7
Waiting for Uncle Sam *Second Prize*	Larry Sanders Dallas, Texas	15
Go Army! *Third Prize (Tie)*	Lynda Palmer Atlanta, Georgia	22
Come the Revolution *Third Prize (Tie)*	Scooter Smith Dallas, Texas	27
The Letter *Honorable Mention*	J. Allen Whitt Albuquerque, New Mexico	34
The Bunker *Honorable Mention*	Robert Swandby Boise, Idaho	36
Marching to a Different Drummer *Honorable Mention*	Gordon Smith Hot Springs, Arkansas	45
I, The Ensign *Honorable Mention*	Susan Lindsley Decatur, Georgia	49

Surveillance — Gered Beebe — 55
Recognized — San Diego, California

Maggie Takes the Constellation — Marguerite F. McDole — 63
Recognized — McKinney, Texas

The Deceptively Slow Motion of Impinging Low Pressure — Frank Light — 72
Recognized — Issaquah, Washington

Ageless Authors Bonus Selections — 73

Nelson Rankin Learns How to Retire — Larry Upshaw — 75
Executive Director

A Reading Anthology of Writers Age 65+ — Jean Yeager — 80
Consultant

Dang, I Wish I Hadn't Done That (Regrets) — 85

The Klutzwit Gene — Geoffrey Graves — 87
First Prize — Laguna Beach, California

In the Midst of Life — Marc Hess — 96
Second Prize — Fredericksburg, Texas

Morning Thunder — Richard Perreault — 104
Third Prize — Bryson City, North Carolina

That Ol' Certainty — John Hunter — 111
Honorable Mention — Rutland, Vermont

Words and When I Knew Them — Nancy Meyer — 115
Honorable Mention — Portola Valley, California

Aging — Brenda Mutchnick — 118
Honorable Mention — Beverly Hills, California

The Crux — Tank Gunner — 121
Honorable Mention — Duncanville, Texas

Summer of '61 — Joe Crawford — 126
Honorable Mention — Toccoa, Georgia

An Arrested Development — Terri Elders — 134
Recognized — Westminster, California

The Babe in the Box — Richard Perreault — 142
Honorable Mention — Bryson City, North Carolina

Parents, For Better or Worse — 151

Moon of the Popping Trees — Hugh Gardner — 153
First Prize — Idledale, Colorado

Mr. Joiner's Puppies — Evelyn Neil — 161
Second Prize — Albuquerque, New Mexico

A Proper Mother — Maureen Kellen-Taylor — 167
Third Prize — Fort Worth, Texas

The Broken Watch — Tank Gunner — 173
Honorable Mention — Duncanville, Texas

Plaques — Robert Nelis — 178
Honorable Mention — Chicago, Illinois

Seven is the Magic Number **Kenneth Stewart** **184**
Honorable Mention Collierville, Tennessee

Exits and Entrances **Hedda Herzog** **191**
Honorable Mention Berkeley, California

Among Kindred Strangers **James Spence** **200**
Honorable Mention Decatur, Georgia

The White Blouse **Brenda Guyton** **207**
Recognized Dallas, Texas

All That Matters **Penny Michalski** **211**
Recognized Middleton, Massachusetts

Special Poetry Prize 213

The Door Gunner **J. Allen Whitt** **215**
Albuquerque, New Mexico

Judging Team 219

Team Leaders **221**
Team Members **222**

Introduction

"The worst curse in life is unlimited potential."

THE PERSON CREDITED WITH SAYING THIS IS A PERFECT EXample of unlimited potential in action. At age 19, Ken Brett was the youngest player ever to pitch in a World Series. He was considered the wunderkind of his time. And to us mere mortals of less than major league ability, his 14-year career indicates that he did well for himself.

It's just that during his career, he was shunted around to 10 different teams. Brett was considered good enough to be in the majors, but not a guy you *had* to have on your roster. Trade bait. The last guy to be waived. And to make matters worse for him, he crafted a mediocre record as his younger brother, George Brett, fashioned a Hall of Fame career. Ken Brett relished his potential for greatness and lived with the disappointment of never actually reaching it, hence the curse.

Potential in life often relates to where you start and how far above or below that starting point you reach. We can wonder about families who practically disown a child who selects a major public university when Harvard is the family standard.

Joking, I say that I was the prodigal child of my family because I didn't carry a gun to school. No one looked to my family for greatness, so I came off pretty good.

When I consider those I've known personally who were cursed with unlimited potential, my late friend Jim Gregory is my prime example. We met in the seventh grade on the Gaston Junior High Warriors football team. He was the right guard and I was the left, but Jim was twice the athlete I was—faster, stronger, muscled up to my Pillsbury Doughboy. At Bryan Adams High School in Dallas, we played in a band together. I was a pitchy lead singer while Jim developed into a masterful blues guitar player.

After graduating from high school in 1965, a year in college and two in the military, Jim went into sales. It was the natural job for a guy with personality, good looks and no degree. As they say, women loved him and men wanted to be him. Jim could sell anything if he was "on" that day. But he was restless and constantly dissatisfied with his life. Jim had difficulty concentrating on anything or anyone for a sustained period. What he had was natural talent, especially an ability to make people laugh, and he enjoyed the attention that brought him. He frequented comedy clubs and tried his hand at standup comedy. Pretty soon, he was touring the country in a circuit with a cadre of funnymen. But Jim was never the headliner, and it frustrated him.

Clearly he wanted fame and fortune, but he always traveled a hard road to get there. When everyone our age was flipping out over The Beatles and the Rolling Stones, he could match licks with Leadbelly, Josh White and Big Bill Broonzy. His blues artistry didn't impress girls in a culture that simply wanted to "hold your hand."

I wrote a lot of comedy material for my friend, and watched him perform many times, but I never had the intestinal fortitude to take the stage. I admired his courage for even trying and saw him die a thousand deaths when a bit didn't translate. Few places are more lonely than the standup comedy stage, but that's where he went.

In his single days, his relations with women were equally perplexing. A ruggedly handsome guy, he would walk into a room full of attractive women and 99% of them would take notice of him. He would, of course, concentrate on those guaranteed *not* to respond to him. Sometimes, with his looks and great sense of humor, he could break down the defenses of an entire room.

Eventually, Jim married and he and his wife had a son. After bouncing around to various jobs, Jim settled into the realization that he would never have the level of fame he desired. For himself and his family, he would concentrate on making money. He read books about getting rich quick and became convinced he had the stuff to make it big. In pursuit of money, he skirted closer to the bare edges of the law, buying and reselling merchandise in questionable ways and getting to know some unsavory people. During this time, Jim drifted farther from his family and friends.

We found out in time that he had become a mid-level operative in a large criminal enterprise, in charge of moving thousands of pounds of marijuana from Texas to the Northeast each month. And that career choice led to approximately five harrowing years in federal prison. Jim came out of the slammer alive but just barely. All he wanted to do was live his life and become a better father to his now-grown son. It became apparent to those of us around him that his experiences in prison and years of abusing different substances had taken their toll.

Jim was a spent man, both mentally and physically, and he tried to content himself with jobs an ex-con is allowed to undertake, such as dishwasher and weekend omelet maker. He was never an easy person to claim as a friend, with his bi-polar*ish* ups and downs and his absences for months on end. But he clung tenuously to his new life, and I was determined to help him find something that might add a little meaning to it.

I had been asked by a regional publisher here in Texas to suggest a book I would like to write for her. I had recently been around some other high school chums and the subject of regrets came to mind. Seems like everyone had varying cases of "woulda, shoulda, coulda" and how those decisions changed their lives. I set out to write a book on the regrets we all have and my friend Jim Gregory certainly had the experience to be co-author.

I did some preliminary research and set parameters for Jim to follow in collecting the regrets of other people. It was mostly starting on Google and making his way through various databases, the kind of research that almost anyone could do. After a couple of months of frustration, erratic starts and almost no progress, though, Jim had uncovered very little of the information needed for the book. But he had a plan, the kind of plan only my friend could conjure up.

"I have it," he said. "We call the book *DANG, I Wish I Hadn't Done That.*"

"Okay, good title," I said. "What else?"

Jim was sure this would fly. "You know those books that don't have anything on the inside pages?"

I didn't care for the direction this discussion was taking.

"We make this look like a book, but there's no words on the inside," he said. "That's the joke. Get it?" Getting the information proved too difficult, so he took a different road.

It was probably inevitable that the book of regrets would stall. Soon after, Jim became very ill. After a lengthy hospital stay, he died of congestive heart failure.

Still he left me with a catchy title, and now I get to use it as a tribute to him. First, *DANG, I Wish I Hadn't Done That* made the light of day as a category in our 2018 Ageless Authors Writing Contest, along with *Military Memories* and *Parents, For Better or Worse.*

Now, in honor of my late friend, it becomes the title of this collection of the best work from that writing contest. From the more than 350 submissions to our contest, we selected 34 stories and poems guaranteed to gain and keep your interest. It is certainly more than regrets. It is a compelling group of works from writers age 65 and older gathered in one volume.

This book includes the powerful coming-of-age essay *Moon of the Popping Trees* by Bivona Prize winner Hugh Gardner of Idledale, Colorado; *The Klutzwit Gene,* the story of a family project gone awry that won the DANG category for Geoffrey Graves of Laguna Beach, California; and *Refugee,* a rather unusual military adventure by Leah Rae Lake of Austin, Texas. This book features life-long professional writers as well as those who became dedicated to the craft in retirement. They are all great storytellers, and in a sense they are realizing the ambitions of my friend Jim Gregory to live up to their potential.

Dang, I'm glad we did this.

Larry Upshaw
Editorial Director
Ageless Authors

MILITARY MEMORIES

Refugee

Leah Rae Lake

First Place

SHE HAD TIME. THEY WERE COMING. THE MORNING NEWS was filled with frantic reports that the unthinkable had occurred. For a moment, she sensed a slight vibration under her feet. Thunder, perhaps, or them. She absently fingered the heavy packet of black silk brocade in her lap. Thirty-five dollars a yard, but worth it.

She'd sensed their movement a week ago, but you could never be certain about timing. Lifting off the wooden top of her great-grandmother's treadle sewing machine, she sighed, gazing out the open door into the warm morning sunshine. Her flower garden was unusually beautiful this year, almost perfect. No, it wouldn't be long now. She'd already sorted what she would need but first, the skirt.

> *Standing far off at the raw edge of a high mountain road she could just make out the smoke from the valley where her house once stood. Black snaking smoke from several closer buildings and growing blemishes of fire in the town below. It was gone. All but the memories. As she watched the smoking destruction stretching below, she felt her memories slipping away.*

Giving up jeans would be hard, but she could see no way around it. And no panties. She needed to be able to lift her skirt to pee in the weeds and still have privacy with people around. And there would be people, for a while. At least a skirt wouldn't stink in the crotch with a month's wear, like pants. That's what she figured, a month or two on the road.

After filling the bullet bobbin, she squinted close to the needle and threaded it with black silk. She inhaled the distinctive smell of machine oil, so like an old friend. If she'd had children, she would have invested in one of those computerized machines with a self-threader. But this was good enough for taking in and letting out waists and hems. She wasn't hard enough on clothes to need repairs. Shaken out, the dark material rippled and shone in her hands, flowing over her lap like oil.

She had no paper pattern, only a picture in her mind. A longish skirt, short enough to climb, full enough to sit cross-legged on the ground. She decided on a drawstring waist, knowing she would lose weight. Elastic wouldn't stand up in the wilds. A short lining with hidden pockets. And deep side pockets, like those in men's trousers. She knew about men's pants. She smiled, knowing her friends were amused by her multiple divorces, while she mostly remembered the honeymoons. Yes, luxurious pockets so deep things wouldn't fall out on the ground as she slept.

Her fingers flew. Within the hour she was turning slowly before the bedroom mirror, hands deep in the pockets of the black skirt. So graceful. What a shame it would soon be frayed and dirty. No matter. Laid out on the bed were faded silk long johns from some forgotten ski trip. Even summer nights could be cold in the hills. Layered silk was windproof and weighed almost nothing. If only she were young, and stronger, but it couldn't be helped. As her fingers stroked the silken undergarments, her mind flashed forward.

> *Her toes were like ice. She pulled on another pair of socks, rubbing her feet briskly. The faint smoke from dying campfires across the creek made her wonder if she should have joined the others. But a croupy cough, a child's whining cry and angry voices quickly*

dissipated her brief nostalgia for company. Low flying clouds whipped passed stars with such speed she grew dizzy from an acute sense of planetary movement. Or maybe it was the stomach cramps and diarrhea that wracked her earlier. No more eating grass. With a sigh, she laid back against the soft purse. Shivering extra hard to warm herself, she tried again to sleep.

The black long johns slid through her fingers into a silky heap on the bed, rousing her from the brief vision. From under the bed, she pulled out a small, cardboard carton of supplies. To the six pairs of men's sox (nylon to dry quickly, and black, so she wouldn't see the dirt), she added a wool pair. A dark wash cloth for a towel. Toothbrush, no paste. She'd make do.

She fingered tightly sealed packets of dried sweet peas and bite-sized jerky and ham. Small bites so she wouldn't be noticed eating. The box reeked of the pungent sweetness of dried carrots. She would eat them first. Looking around the comfortable bedroom, her chest tightened. Walking out onto the deck, she watered a vividly pink geranium on the window sill. It would die without her. With a sigh, she returned to her sewing and quickly finished a cover for the thin foam bedroll. It would have to do.

Spreading the remaining black brocade out on the pale carpet, she planned where and how to cut out the big purse she would carry, a sort of heavily gathered duffel with hidden pockets. Commercial backpacks didn't meet her needs, not by a long shot. To line it against drenching spring rains and mud, she chose a slick fabric, impervious to cold or water. Yesterday, not finding the fabric itself, she first bought herself a jacket, then three more, men's size XXXL, and cut out the backs for lining. The expense didn't seem to matter as she would not likely be here when the bill arrived.

Looking for scissors, she walked into the kitchen, flexing her new state-of-the-art hiking boots. She put a cup of water in the microwave to boil, grateful she still had electricity. That wouldn't last long. She really would miss her Earl Gray. Inhaling the fragrant tea bag, her eyes stung from the poignancy of the moment. Rummaging in a drawer, she found the pointed Joyce Chen boning shears. Sharper than sewing scissors, the large red plastic handles made them a perfect tool. She snapped them absently a time or two, planning a special pocket to hold them. Tea was ready. A few tea bags wouldn't weigh much. Not as much as these scissors which she would plunge into the neck of that awful man as he tried to rape her.

> *She hadn't anticipated his weight, or his seemingly endless convulsions. He collapsed so suddenly that his torso pinned her down. Her throat throbbed where his thumbs bruised her neck. She gasped for air, but couldn't move him. Blood splattered so noisily in great pulses on nearby leaves that she prayed no one would wake. Her brain tingled from lack of oxygen, and she imagined being found dead in the morning with this fat man draped across her. His vile, pungent odor of stale sweat gave her strength. She rocked him enough to squirm out, pulling her skirt with both hands. Rolling him off her mat, she wiped the sticky wetness as best she could. Time to go. She hoped black would hide dried blood stains.*

Still gripping the scissors, she carefully set her tea on the corner of the sewing machine and began to cut. Two strong shoulder straps, in case one broke, padded for comfort. The machine clacked and whirred as she peddled and stitched, trying not to think of what she would lose. When they were long, black tubes, she rolled several twenties from the box and stuffed them in, hoping existing currency might survive the terror, followed by her few rings and small pins which mattered. Then, carefully, she fed in her lovely natural pearl necklace, an expensive anniversary present from one of her husbands. She stroked each cool pearl with her fingertips as she pushed it into the strap.

> *The girl's hands were smooth and white as she touched her throat, almost as white as the pearls. And plump. She'd forgotten hands could look like that. She looked at her own thin, chapped hands and dirt-stained nails. When had they changed? She couldn't remember. She*

watched the girl's husband fasten the pearls around her neck, knowing how it felt. The girl smiled. The young couple had rented this isolated hunting lodge through a magazine ad, and were completely out of touch. How sweet and sheltered they were. Exchanging the pearls for a shower, bed, and a few hot meals, was a bargain.

As the last pearl was tucked safely up the strap end, she looked slowly around her room. Her vision blurred as she tried to pin together soft pieces of black silk. Reminding herself that she cried where no loss had yet occurred, and that these were only "things," didn't help. Her memories were embodied in the house itself. If she lost the house, she might lose a part of who she was. She suddenly had a new thought.

She slammed the presser-foot down, pushing the silk tight against sharp metal teeth. Her right foot pumped, and as the frame shook slightly, the needle began to stitch. Picking up the rhythm, she noticed her favorite rocking chair from the corner of her eye. She loved that chair. Wanting to take it with her, she mentally transferred her image of the chair into each stitch. Glancing again, the chair solidly sat where it always sat. The machine stopped as she slumped and frowned. Then putting both feet square on the treadle, with both hands guiding the fabric, she tried again. Holding the idea of a chair while clearly visualizing the chair itself, she smelled the cream leather, felt the funny wrinkles, and caressed the slight roughness of age on the arms where her fingers played. To her joy, the chair shimmered slightly and faded away. Yes!

She ran swift, mental fingers over blue bathroom tile, and admired the fragile translucence of her white china. She mentally gathered her thick photo albums, smelled the white fluffy towels, and enjoyed the cozy fireplace that warmed her winter nights. Remembering the texture and color of each wall, the special flaws in the Persian rugs, she embraced tall windows set to catch the light just so. She thought of the new roof, and her car in the freshly painted, white garage. Faster and faster, guiding the fabric, she wove the things she loved into the clickety-clack of each stitch as rooms misted and faded behind her. She smiled at her favorite books, rock music and jazz, and cut-glass vases. The black machine vibrated and rocked, as the speeding turn-wheel fanned her face.

Finally, it was done. In silence, she knotted and clipped the final threads. With trembling fingers, she slid the scissors into their new pocket. The purse looked almost professional, more practical than she'd hoped. Straps at the bottom tightly held the black bedroll. Velcro pockets were everywhere. She didn't trust zippers in the mud. And there would be mud. And cold fingers. And broken nails.

The teacup rattled in its saucer. She twisted toward the muffled booms. There were sounds like firecrackers in the distance. They were close. Soon she would have to leave. She pulled the box around and began transferring packets to the new bag. She knew exactly where each item belonged.

A pity she dared not share her small provisions. It went against her nature, but then again, her generous nature had never before run up against her instinct for survival. A heavy, flexible water pouch with covered straw, slipped into the inner lining, provided emergency water which she could drink unnoticed. There would soon be thousands heading for the hills, tens of thousands.

She stopped with the last packet in her hands, a packet of tiny envelopes of seed for the deepest heart of the purse. Beans, onions, herbs galore, squash, chilies, corn, cucumbers. And flower seed. Especially flowers.

> *A drop of rain running down a loose strand of hair stung her eye. As she moved to wipe it, she saw that her hands were muddy. Rinsing them in the warm rain, she was satisfied with the number of weeds she'd pulled today. Surrounding the healthy, growing vegetables, a few flowers were already blooming. Seeing her bare footprints in the dark, loamy soil, she curled her toes in the mud. It felt cool and smooth. A red ladybug crawled up her forearm, and she whispered, "Ladybug, ladybug, fly away home, your house is on fire and your children will burn," and it flew off. She saw no people, but it didn't matter. The air smelled of growing things and new beginnings.*

Her thumb still stroked the plastic packet of seeds, seeds of her future. Her own future felt somehow like the future of humankind. Briskly, she sealed the inner pocket. Several twigs rattled down through the leaves of a nearby cottonwood. She glanced across the valley to the distant freeway, choked with cars. Most would soon walk, refugees in their own country. She wondered idly why she hadn't left days ago, but it wasn't important now.

Dropping the empty box, she was amazed to notice that her sewing machine now rested alone on a large square of fresh dirt in the midst of an otherwise empty lawn. She stood to go, then paused. Sighing, she raised her black skirt, pulled down and stepped out of her white panties. They seemed unnaturally bright in the sunlight. She expected to feel vulnerable but the sudden awareness of her body lifted her spirits. The unexpected sensation of cool air between her thighs felt somehow adventurous, liberating. Almost reverently, she folded the panties and left them under the saucer. The ground rocked violently, and the empty cup rolled over noisily. On impulse, she popped the delicate cup into the purse. Hoisting the bag, she looped long black straps over her head and across her chest. Striding purposefully across the manicured lawn, patting the bag, her fingers found comfort sliding sensuously up and down the smooth black silk.

> *Newly rooted with far fewer belongings, growing and hoping to flourish, she realized it doesn't matter where you live or by what you are surrounded. These are all just things. Emotions may feel the "pain of change" but the heart is never touched by loss of stuff. Each of us is a creative force, and no matter our surroundings, re-creating the beauty that resides within us brings us quickly home again.*

Pausing at the edge of the yard, she again slipped out her scissors. No shadow crossed her mind this time. Clipping a handful of her freshest yellow roses, carefully trimming the thorns, she started up the hill. Burying her face in their fragrance, she didn't look back. The past was gone. Her future bounced gently against her hip.

Leah Rae Lake, a frequently published writer based in Austin, Texas, delights in doing things her way and following her subjective curiosity. This creative freedom led her into some fascinating searches and adventures. She's dabbled with many creative media: painting, poetry, comic strips, radio programs, nonfiction articles, playwriting, even stand-up comedy as a quick post-divorce restorative. Seeking deeper creativity, fortunately she discovered the true creative medium for any enlightened person is not just writing but transforming their own life. She's eagerly finishing her first books: *Being: Beyond Spiritual Relativity* and *Little Tree Grows and Grows and Grows.*

Waiting for Uncle Sam

Larry Sanders

Second Prize

I RECEIVED TWO LETTERS FROM UNCLE SAM SOON AFTER my 18th birthday. The first letter informed me I was required to register for the draft. In that letter I was told to report at precisely 6 A.M. to the basement floor of an old building in downtown Little Rock.

"Please do not be late!"

It was a cold wet Saturday morning when I nervously joined a group of about 50 other young men, where we all waited in silence before being divided into smaller groups.

After hours of marching around in our underwear from one cold room to the next and given every imaginable medical exam possible from head to toe, we were told to get dressed. We then silently filed into an adjoining larger room full of rows of desks, where we were given various written aptitude and mental questionnaires.

Just before the group of us was released in late afternoon, we were told to expect a letter in the mail sometime in the near future. They couldn't tell us how long we would have to wait, but were advised to inform the United States Draft Board immediately of any updates that might effect our current status. Changes such as address relocation, education, marital or family status or any new health issues. They wanted to keep tabs on us for as long as possible.

I was still living at home and sacking groceries for minimum wage at a national chain store about five miles from our house. Since I had very little money after paying rent to my parents and no money for a car, I shared an old used rusty Rambler in need of many repairs with my mother. She and my father had just given me my own personal set of car keys wrapped up in a small box, wishing me Happy Birthday. I was touched because I knew they must have sat down at the kitchen table together to discuss what to get me since neither of them had much money. They worked different times and rarely saw each other except when they were drinking or arguing over financial matters.

I drove to and from work each day, only stopping to make sure the car had enough gas before handing it over to my mother. She was 40 years old and still called Babydoll, a nickname from her youth. She continued to perm and bleach her hair, trying to keep that youthful look. She worked the evening shift, waiting on tables at the restaurant at the Ramada Inn Motel located about 10 miles down the interstate.

My mother always got home very late after we had already gone to bed. After parking the car in the driveway, she would sit down at the kitchen table to smoke one last cigarette and count out her tips before going to bed. She left lunch money for my sister and brother who got themselves off to school each morning while she slept in. This automobile relay routine that my mother and I shared continued each and every day, until I got the second letter I was promised from Uncle Sam.

That particular afternoon I arrived home a little late from my job at the grocery store after stopping to put $2 worth of gas in the car. My father was waiting for me as I pulled into the dirt driveway. He was in the front yard leaning next to his car, deep in thought while looking down at an open letter held tightly in his hand, which was still slowly flapping in the breeze. The look on his face was one I had never seen before. He was pale and without emotion as he tried not looking at me as I climbed out of the car.

"Hi Daddy, what's up? Is everything okay?"

"This letter is for you, son. Hope you don't mind me opening it?" He said still looking downward.

I knew instantly what this letter contained and was not bothered that my father had opened my personal mail. It was the second letter I had been dreading for months, ever since that early morning physical.

The letter arrived almost four months to the day after registering at the draft board. It was printed on very official United States Government letterhead informing me I had been drafted into the United States Army. It also gave the date of departure and where I would be sent for training. I had six weeks to get my life in order before I reported to the Greyhound Bus Depot in downtown Little Rock. There I would board a bus, along with other inductees, to Fort Campbell, Kentucky for eight weeks of combat basic training.

My father was a Navy veteran of WWII, serving almost eight years in the Pacific. He dropped out of school and enlisted at 16, after lying about his age. Most of his memories and stories of that time he kept to himself. I was sure he left as an innocent young boy, full of dreams, and returned to face reality as an older and much different man. He, of all people, knew what that letter represented. The military would change me as it had changed him. Opening that letter addressed to me from Uncle Sam was his way of saying how concerned he was.

My father, at 45, was just over six feet tall. He had muscles from years of hard construction work. They were covered with faded tattoos from his travels in the military. He was normally a very quiet man except when he drank.

Years and years of heavy drinking turned him from a hardworking loving husband and father into a larger than life frightening stranger who cursed and raged with anger and hatred. I'm sure he expected alcohol would help keep the demons from his past buried deep down in a place where they could never be felt. But it didn't go as hoped. It actually helped release his feelings, bringing them outward with violent anger, lashing out at family, friends, or whoever was in the way. His drinking always began on Friday afternoons during his long drive home from work, first with a six pack of cold beer, changing quickly to cheap whiskey once he got home and would not stop until Monday morning. Smiles and laughter, after the first few glasses of alcohol, quickly changed into seething storms of curse words full of annoyance, resentment and blind outrage. He eventually passed out in his bed. I had been cursed out or physically threatened so many times that I quickly learned to stay out of his way, especially over those weekends.

My father's heavy drinking, two packs a day of unfiltered cigarettes and an unhappy daily life, mixed with buried pain from his past and lost dreams would eventually take his life within three years.

Both my parents, with very little education, were trying their best to support and raise a family of five. Together they watched their marriage crumble from various rent houses and an assortment of low paying jobs. My mother, never finishing high school, had been bouncing back and forth from waiting on tables to working at a variety of small factory jobs since she was a teenager. Arguing over what bills to pay, and facing different hardships that lay ahead, she soon discovered it was much easier to just join my father on those alcoholic binges where they both tried to shut out the past and ignore the future.

It was a very strange time back then for all of us. My younger sister and brother, who were still going to school, always kept to themselves faraway from the house. My parents, working different shifts, were relating less and less while drinking more and more. I was still sacking groceries. The country was in the middle of a war no one knew anything about. We all just continued our daily routines, never looking up to notice each other. It seemed safer that way.

If any of us watched the war on the small black and white TV, we watched in silence, keeping our thoughts to ourselves. We never acknowledged any of our family's turmoil and uncertainty even though it had moved in, becoming a permanent resident.

We didn't discuss the country's disruption over Vietnam either, even though it was already knocking on our front door. The war was never brought up. Current events and politics were for others to discuss who felt they had a voice, not us. Channels were changed if televised battles became too bloody and newspaper articles were skipped if they gave too much information. Questions were never asked because there were no answers.

Why are we fighting a war half way around the world in a strange land? Why are we sending our children and friends to their deaths? Who got us into this war? How long could it possibly last?

My mother chose not to discuss the war because it represented the present, knowing very well she was powerless to do anything about it. My father chose not to discuss the war because it represented the past and touched upon buried emotions he hoped to forget. I chose not to discuss Vietnam because it represented the future and I might be thrust into the middle of it.

Eventually the war entered our house, resulting in more chaos, while causing my parents to drift farther apart. My father's drinking advanced from weekend rituals to nightly events where he retreated early each evening into his bedroom. My mother's drinking also progressed on weekends after her late night shift ended where she met up with old girlfriends at nearby bars.

I just waited fearfully, knowing the war could change my life forever and expose my secrets. Eighteen years of secrets of fear and shame. Secrets I never shared or acted on except in my thoughts.

Secrets I had tried to hide soared to the surface months before, during the day of the draft registration. It was almost like an interrogation. Information was required with very personal answers. Somewhere in the middle of one of the surveys was a question I had been dreading.

I had heard that some kind of question like this existed but was still shocked to see it. "Do you identify as a homosexual or ever had sexual feelings for persons of the same sex?" Yes or No. Pick one box now and check it! There was not even a "Maybe" or "Not Sure" box.

Wow! They didn't mess around at the draft board. They wanted to know everything! How could a little box barely big enough to hold an X from my pencil have so much power? Which box do you check or maybe leave blank? This little box could change my future. For better or worse. Of course it was an easy way out. But you had to live with the consequences, whatever they were.

No one seemed to know what happened to the young men who checked that box. Were they ever seen again? Were they released into the general population? Or worse yet, would they be known as homosexuals with a big "QUEER" on their back like the adulteress Hester Prynne in the Scarlet Letter? It was frightening!

At that time being known as a queer was worse than being drafted and possibly killed in action in a "screwed up" war no one understood. What about my friends and family? How do I explain how I got out of the draft? Flat feet, asthma, or just too dumb to pass the tests?

This little box in the middle of the written test was almost jumping off the page with a life of its own. This box could destroy lives or extend lives. Oh my God, this little box was powerful! There was no one I could consult to make this last-minute decision. Just quickly check it yes or no. What do I do?

If I checked the "Yes" box, I most likely would be singled out within this group of unknown young men and marched into a private office while they called my parents.

"Do you know your son is a homosexual?" Oh god! So much was going through my head.

I had known I was different since I was a little boy but couldn't prove anything. I had never been touched or kissed in all my 18 years. It was all based on my secret feelings. Feelings I grew up realizing I must always keep private and never tell anyone, especially family and friends. So with no information and a lot of fear, I quickly decided to check the "No" box. Oh god, what now?

My father and I had never been close. We had little in common. The last time my father and I really talked to each other was over two years before when I was in the eleventh grade. We found ourselves suddenly standing together in total silence on our small concrete back porch at the previous rent house. I didn't know what got into me but I blurted out to him that I knew what I wanted to do with the rest of my life. "I want to go to art school when I graduate," I said, hoping he would be excited for me.

Instead he looked at me with his familiar frustrated look. "Get it out of your goddamn head! We can't afford college!" He turned around and walked back into the house after slamming the screen door. I just stood there looking at the plain back yard, not ready to go back inside.

The afternoon I returned home from sacking groceries was different.

As I drove into the driveway, I could tell my father had been waiting outside. He slowly handed me the letter without looking at me. "Son, this is for you. I'm sorry, but I had to open it. I recognized what it was. I'm so sorry."

He now silently watched my face as I read the official letter informing me I had been drafted into the United States Army. I folded the letter, slipping it back into the envelope as we walked back to the house in silence. We continued our quietness and stillness as we both sat down in front of the TV to watch the evening news. Looking across the room at his face I no longer saw a man aged beyond his years, but saw someone very different. I now recognized his vulnerability, his youth, his sadness, his pain and his unfulfilled dreams from years gone by. I saw a man trying to connect before it was too late.

We were no longer father and son as we sat there in silence. We were now brothers. It was the first time and the last time I felt close to my father.

Larry Sanders' memories of actual events and the interesting people from his early life, as well as his time in combat, are stories that he has never been able to tell until now. Larry was born in Little Rock, Arkansas in 1947 and served in the U.S. Army during the Vietnam War (1967-1969). He holds a BA in Fine Arts, spent 20 years as an art director and sixteen years as owner of a Mexican folk art store. He is recently retired and lives in Dallas, Texas.

Go Army!

Lynda Palmer

Third Place (Tie)

TWENTY MINUTES LATER AND I WOULD HAVE BEEN IN THE air and on my way to basic training. Instead, I was sitting at the gate retained by security. Two Army MPs held my recruiter, Robert Christiansen, yelling at him like the idiot he was that day.

"Who do you think you are?'

"You can kiss your Army career goodbye."

"The FBI is on their way."

Oh great. Not only am I in big trouble with the Army, but I may well end up in prison on a federal rap. I sighed while trying to look away from the scene. *How did I get myself into this mess,* I thought, knowing the answer full well.

Three months earlier, I walked into the Army recruitment center and signed up on the spot. It seemed like all I could do. I had run out of money to finish college and felt like I had to get away from home. My home life was not a disaster, but I was spending most of my time tending to my brothers and sisters. If I didn't get away soon, I would end up caring for them the rest of my life.

Before heading to the recruitment office, I considered my military options. Seasickness was my curse, so the Navy and Coast Guard were out. I couldn't see myself as a jarhead. My sinus problems would keep me from being a pilot, and that was the only job I wanted to do in the Air Force. So, the Army it was. This was 1974, and our buildup in Vietnam had come to a close. The chances of us getting into another conflict in the next three years were slim. Besides, the opportunities for training and life experiences were immeasurable.

Entering the recruitment office, I saw a small room containing two desks with phones and computers on top. Each had a holder with Go Army! on it, filled with pencils. On the wall, posters of a soldier decked out in full gear told me to "Be all that you can be." In the corner was a cooler with water and soda and a machine giving off the odor of burned coffee.

Behind the first desk sat a soldier, Edwards, his nametag said. He was a corporal in training to be a recruitment sergeant.

"Can I help you?" he asked, looking up at me.

"I want to enlist."

"Just like that." Surprise covered his face.

I guess they don't get many women walking in to sign up, but I needed him to understand I was serious about it. Before I went into my lengthy explanation, I was interrupted by another soldier coming out of a back room.

"Ask the lady to sit down, Corporal."

In your mind, if you ever pictured GI Joe coming alive, this was the man. Tall, muscular, with a spectacular smile that filled his face, he had perfect teeth, perfect hair, smelled great and filled his uniform in all the right places. I sat down, aware that I was locked into a swoon.

Get a grip, girl. You're here for one purpose, and he is not it. I didn't believe my own thoughts.

"So, what makes you imagine you'll make a good soldier?"

I began to process the question. I was here to enlist and get to training. The thought of being a soldier and what that meant was a little beyond me.

"Well, I'm a team player, I can follow instructions, and I have faith in the U.S."

Having acted as the peacemaker in my family, I wasn't sure I was combat material. Rarely did I get my way in the family. Because of that, I surmised there was some hidden aggression deep down just waiting to be released.

"Haven't thought much about it, have you?" he said. "If you don't mind me saying, you are not the typical female recruit."

"What do you mean?' I asked.

"You're white, educated, good looking and don't seem dirt poor."

"Thanks, I guess. I'm out of money for school and I've run out of places to go. I can't go home and take care of my brothers and sisters forever."

"Okay, let's get started."

Two hours later, I had chosen my desired training as an orthopedic technician, taken some tests and signed away three years of my life. Now, all I needed was to tell my family.

My parents took the news okay. Dad seemed proud of me, and to my surprise, Mom said she secretly wanted to run away to the Army when she was younger, but it wasn't allowed.

I left the recruiting office with writer's cramp and a date with GI Joe, er... Bob. He told me he hadn't done this before, and I wanted to trust him. But I was mature enough to know that as a recruiter he had the perfect opportunity to screen potential love interests. The not-so-subtle flirting going on between us could not be ignored. Granted, I was in a significant dating slump, and he possessed those fine attributes, which made me agree to go out with him.

We spent the three months before basic training behaving like teenagers. It started with movies, walks in the park and dinner. With little time, we progressed rapidly around the bases. It was fun searching for our next rendezvous and thrilling to make the best of them. Outside at the park, a backroom at the office, a friend's home, and the rare hotel room served as tryst locations. Not having an apartment, we put up with cold floors, wood chips, bruises, and interruptions. We enjoyed each other at every opportunity and in every way.

A week from reporting for basic, Bob and I were an item.

"I can get you out of this," Bob pleaded. "You don't belong in the Army. You can stay here with me."

This became his constant plea. I considered it, as I was fast becoming crazy about him. My answer was always the same, though. I wasn't ready to settle down yet, and I wouldn't renege on my commitment.

I was bound to go through with it. Besides, I couldn't help seeing this as an adventure. It was my way out of my big sister life and the freedom I craved.

The night before we boarded our plane to basic training, all recruits were put up in a hotel after saying our goodbyes to friends and families. At the hotel, some girls cried, others reached out to meet fellow recruits, and I joined a group old enough to share a drink or two as it would be our last until training was over.

Bob tried one last time to convince me of the error of my choice.

"Enough Bob," I said. "If it was such a bad decision, why did you sign me up in the first place?"

He paused. "Quotas. I was way under for that month. Besides, I didn't know you then."

"It can't be as bad as you predict. I'll see you when I get leave."

I didn't want to think about it again. Walking up the stairs to the plane, I looked back at Bob. GI Joe never looked so pitiful. Then before we could take off, I heard my name announced and they escorted me off. That's how I got into this mess.

Bob told them I was not a real soldier and my being on the plane was a threat to national security. At the gate, confusion ensued. I was in some kind of deep trouble. All I knew was I could trace it back to Bob.

"I guess I didn't use my head this time. I suppose I blew my Army career and I got you in trouble," Bob said as he sat next to me.

"I've been in worse trouble," I lied.

Just then, an officer with some impressive insignia of rank arrived, informing the MPs he would handle it. He escorted us away from the gate.

"Both of you come with me." I didn't know him, but you could tell he meant business. He and Bob undeniably knew each other.

The officer escorted us to a waiting limousine. I did not understand what was going on until Bob got on one knee.

"You walked into my life three months ago. Now I can't live my life without you. Will you marry me?"

"What about my enlistment? I'm committed."

"Oh, I never put in the paperwork," Bob said sheepishly. "I couldn't figure out how else to keep you in my life until I convinced you we were made for each other."

My expression said it all. It was shock and anger combined. Not an attractive look, I'm sure, but deserved.

"What were you thinking? I enjoy your company but we haven't known each other long enough for this. I enlisted to get money to finish school and escape the life I thought I was trapped in at home."

He looked at me, not believing what he was hearing.

"But I thought..."

"You shouldn't have kept me out of your decision. I'm telling you to get my paperwork done, get me the school you promised, and let me go."

A month later I was in the Army for real. We agreed to see if the future brought anything for us. I jumped headlong into my medical training while Bob showed up at basic training determined to convince my drill sergeants to let me out. His obsession was a bridge too far, as they say. And I stuck with my commitment. Go Army!

Lynda Palmer served among the last Women's Army Corps (WAC) graduates from basic training in 1974. From that time on, the training for men and women was the same. She served for three years as the first female at Ft. Hood, Texas, to work in orthopedics. Then she went back to school as a physician assistant and worked as a PA for more than 30 years. This story is a mostly true account of her enlistment in the Army when her recruiting sergeant even followed her to basic training trying to get her out. But that is the meat of another story. She is an author who has had several articles and short stories published. Retirement has given her the chance to get her stories out there to be enjoyed.

Come the Revolution

SCOOTER SMITH

Third Prize (Tie)

THE ROOM ACROSS THE HALL FROM THE MASTER-AT-ARMS' office exploded into what was clearly a fistfight. Just as suddenly, silence, except for some guttural cursing. A second-class petty officer walked out, brushing himself off. He was a tall, meaty man with a lustrous black mustache and "Martinez" stenciled over the pocket of his denim work shirt. He saw me and a smile lit up his face. "You must be the new guy, Smith."

I nodded. It was dawn, and I had just stepped off the bus from Yakota Air Base to report to my first assignment. After 50-plus hours with little sleep while in transit from San Diego, I felt beat ragged. Following him into his office, I tilted my head toward the recent melee and raised my eyebrows.

"Oh, that," Martinez said. "Just waking up that asshole Janaszek, who can't seem to hear an alarm. He comes up swinging at the poor slob on duty who has to rouse him for his flight back to Cubi."

He noticed my confusion. "To our detachment in Cubi Point, Philippines. Where he's stationed."

Martinez continued: "First time I did it, he hit me without warning, and I hit him back, automatic-like. I thought I'd get court-martialed, but nothing happened. Now, I kind of like to wake him up because I get to punch a jerk who outranks me with no repercussion. Janaszek doesn't remember anything before coffee, and anyway, everyone knows he's a son-of-a-bitch."

Martinez sat down as I sagged under the weight of my sea bag. Sitting open on his desk was a thick book with dozens of torn paper bookmarks hanging down. It was propped up on a copy of Bertrand Russell's *A History of Western Philosophy.*

"Weighty tomes," I said.

"So close to getting my bachelor's degree," Martinez replied. "College man?"

"A year at North Texas State," I replied. "Planning to finish on the GI Bill."

"All right! We'll talk. Let's get you a place to stay, Smitty; then you can check in with Personnel."

"Any chance of getting some sleep?" I asked.

"Tonight. You might as well adjust to time on the other side of the world," Martinez said while looking at a chart on the wall. "Here it is. You're in with Ray Hill."

He rose and motioned for me to follow. We walked down the main hall between cubicles with dark drapes for doors. With a flourish, he opened a curtain. "Hill. Here's Smitty, your new roomie. You good with that?"

A disembodied voice replied, "It's cool."

Martinez turned back to me. "We hope you enjoy your stay."

"Thanks, Martinez."

"Call me Marty," he said, sauntering away.

I stepped into the cubicle and with a sigh of relief let my burden drop. My roommate was standing in front of a hefty green naugahyde chair. He wore the traditional Navy white hat perched atop the beginnings of an afro. His starched and pressed dungaree work shirt sported third class petty officer insignia on its left sleeve. He wore black, Navy issue socks, but no pants. Despite the general gloom of the barracks, he had on heavily tinted glasses with thick black frames. He was holding an open paperback in his left hand.

I introduced myself: "Hi, I'm Scooter Smith. New guy. Uh, nice legs."

Hill said nothing.

"New guy?" I continued. "This rack okay?" I pointed at a bare lower bunk.

Hill spoke: "Smitty, come the revolution, you're gonna have to go up against the wall."

I looked at him askance before inspecting an empty locker. "Well, you wake up cheery."

Hill continued: "You should be aware that because of Vietnam, America is training thousands of black men in all aspects of war. We are learning to speak the white devil's language of violence."

"Everything is hopelessly wrinkled," I said after dumping the contents of my sea bag onto my new bed.

Hill sat down, held up the paperback, and began reading:

"The existence of violence is at the very heart of a racist system. The Afro-American militant is a 'militant' because he defends himself, his family, his home and his dignity. He does not introduce violence into a racist social system—the violence is already there and has always been there. It is precisely the unchallenged violence that allows a racist social system to perpetuate itself. When people say they are opposed to Negroes "resorting to violence," what they really mean is that they are opposed to Negroes defending themselves and challenging the exclusive monopoly of violence practiced by white racists."

Hill's voice had gotten louder, and his hands shook a little toward the end.

"That sounds about right," I said. "So, where you from?"

Ray glared at me, then softened, shaking his head. "Houston. You?"

"Dallas," I replied.

"Texas, too? Where's your redneck accent?" Hill asked. He picked up a pair of dungarees that lay folded on his bed.

"No idea, but I can put it on when I have to deal with bubbas."

"Don't we all," said Hill with a snort. He stood and pulled on his pants.

Meanwhile, I shifted my possessions from the bed to the locker. "Is there a laundromat?" I asked.

"Across the street and down a bit," Hill said, waving his hand in the general direction. He sat back down.

Hill laced up his flight boots as I arranged my stuff.

"I'd like to think that things are changing," I said.

Hill jumped to his feet. "Martin's down, Malcolm's down! JFK and Bobby are down! Angela and Eldridge are on the run! Even the damn writer of this book is on the run! You think things are changing, Smitty? I'll tell you what's changing: Black America has finally realized that political power grows out of the barrel of a gun!"

"Wow, Mao," I said.

"I'm trying to be serious here," Hill said.

"Sorry."

Scowling, Hill said: "That's just disrespect, man. Making a joke out of this is just another example of whitey blowing off the black man's concerns, 'cause you so important and we don't matter!"

He clenched his right fist.

"You waltz in here acting like you own me, just like your great-granddaddy owned my ancestors. I'm... It's just this murdering and terrorizing of my people, it's..." He stopped, sighing in exasperation. His fist relaxed and fell to his side.

I held out my hands: "I'm sorry, Ray. Sorry. Been awake for a couple of days."

Hill collapsed into the chair.

"Look, smart-ass remarks are just me. And I didn't move in here because I think I own you. It's Marty's fault. He assigned me here."

I grinned, but Hill merely stood up and without looking at me reached into his locker and pulled out a gym bag.

"I'm just saying that there's a lot of noise about civil rights," he said softly, "but it ain't manifesting on the street."

He moved his shaving kit and changes of clothes into the bag. I sat at the steel writing desk and turned the chair to face Hill.

"What are you reading?" I asked.

He smirked. "Know many black authors, Smitty?"

"Uh, I'm aware of Ellison, but haven't read him. But I've read the 'Ballots or Bullets' speech by the X guy, and part of Reverend King's 'I Have a Dream' speech."

Hill gasped. "You, a southern white boy, read a speech by Malcolm X?"

I shrugged. "I read a lot."

Hill zipped up the duffel and sat it on the bed. "It's Robert F. Williams' book, *Negros with Guns*."

"Yikes," I said.

"Yeah. The white reaction. Williams talks about that in the book. But all he's saying is that it's the right of all Americans, when the police won't, to act in self-defense against lawless violence."

I nodded. "It is our right, but Reverend King had some things to say about that."

"King is dead," Hill interjected.

"Maybe he died to save our souls."

"Maybe he just got gunned down by a dumb-ass cracker!"

"Maybe both?" I suggested.

Hill paced the cubicle. "Yeah, yeah," he muttered.

"Oh, and I started Cleaver's book, *Soul On Ice*." I made a "so-so" gesture with my right hand.

Hill stopped pacing. "What?"

The doors at the end of the hall banged as they opened and closed. Footsteps echoed. "Hill!" someone called. "Truck's out front. Let's move!"

Ray filled me in: "Doing ops out of Cubi Point. Be back in a couple of weeks."

I nodded. "I'll keep a watch over the place."

"Here," Hill said as he handed *Negros with Guns* to me. "Read it. Tell me what you think."

"Gee. Thanks."

A smile broke across Hill's face. "You know, I like you, Smitty. But come the revolution, you'll still have to go up against the wall."

He turned and walked through the curtain.

With a chuckle, I called out to him: "Nice to meet you, too!"

Hill's short laugh merged into the sharp sound of footsteps on waxed and polished asphalt tile. Doors banged open and shut.

Two days later I wandered into the master-at-arms' office to chat before heading to the hangar. Martinez was slumped in his chair, staring at nothing.

"Marty? You okay?"

He looked much older as he looked up.

"I just heard." He paused. "Just heard. Our flight went down. South China Sea. Approaching the Constellation."

He paused again. Then, almost inaudible, "No survivors."

"Hill?" I asked.

Martinez nodded. I felt a cavernous ache inside.

He continued: "And Dilger, Livingston, Tye." There was a catch in his voice. "And Moser!" A deep sigh rumbled from his chest.

Stunned, I sat down and quietly mourned with Marty. All that day, grief-saturated silence filled the squadron's hangars.

For the next few days, I lived with a phantom roommate. Despite his lack of corporeality, I greeted and said goodbye to Ray as I came and went.

More than that, I read his book.

For the first time, this white, middle-class teenager grasped the soul-crushing degradation that was part and parcel of black life in America; how asking people systematically abused by the commercial and legal establishment to please be patient just further institutionalized that abuse.

Influenced by the ideals of the peace movement, I felt a sense of hopelessness when Williams demonstrated again and again that the threat of retaliatory violence was all too often necessary to prevent violence against peaceful citizens exercising their First Amendment rights.

Most crushing was the unassailable truth that the so-called Christian nation of my birth failed its promise in the century since emancipation.

Four days after receiving the news, the Officer of the Day came to my cubicle with bolt cutters. Martinez followed, carrying strapping tape and a couple of corrugated boxes. I flinched when they cut Ray's lock.

The O.D., Lieutenant Junior Grade Piersanti, carefully removed Ray's personal effects from his locker one by one, announcing aloud what each was. Marty repeated what Piersanti said and recorded the data on a form attached to a clipboard. They filled up one box and began filling another.

I sat on my rack and watched my ghost get exorcised.

After Piersanti passed the last item to Martinez, I stood and handed him *Negros With Guns.* The lieutenant looked at the title and grimaced a bit.

"This is his," I said. "His family needs to have it." I choked a little. "They need to know that, come the revolution, their son was ready to fight for their rights."

Piersanti handed the book to Marty, who noted its title on the form and placed it into the box. As he yanked the tape from its dispenser, it emitted a mournful shriek.

Scooter Smith returned to his first love, writing, after a career as a new media artist. An early computer animator, he helped usher in the digital age with Video Post & Transfer, art-directed for the technologically innovative Dreamtime Imagineering, and functioned as the graphics and IT departments for the online journalistic endeavor, *Moonlady News.* His non-commercial works have shown in the Dallas Video Festival, on KERA's *Frame of Mind,* and in the Dallas Museum of Art exhibition, *DallasSites: Available Space.* In recent years he has devoted time to assisting non-profits as well as writing short stories and memoirs.

The Letter

J. Allen Whitt

Honorable Mention

JOHNNY KRUEGER WAS KILLED AT THE SAWMILL WHEN A load of logs rolled off a logging truck and crushed him. The news reached Quail Creek High School just before lunch. Johnny was 20 and had graduated two years before. The school was small, and all the students knew each other. Johnny, with his gap-tooth smile and joking manner, was a favorite, both in his former school and in the village.

Julie Mitchell and her boyfriend Carl Riley stood together in the school hallway. As tears ran down her cheeks, Julie said, "Oh, it's awful, just awful." Johnny and Julie were cousins. "He and Pam just had a baby, too."

Carl nodded solemnly in agreement. The school's basketball center, he was tall and thin and seemed to tilt forward as he walked, as if leaning into the wind. Carl put his arm around Julie and said, "Yeah, it is, sweetheart. Johnny was a good guy." She shivered and drew the collar of her jacket closer around her neck. It was Carl's basketball letter jacket. He had given it to her that Fall, and she was proud to wear the dark blue jacket with a big red Q on the front.

As the snows of December closed in, Johnny was not there to help put up the town's Christmas tree nor to drape strings of red and green and blue lights on the wooden poles that held Quail Creek's only traffic light.

For Johnny's former schoolmates, his death brought the realization that their days were finite. Soon, many would know death more intimately, as it shredded flesh and tormented minds in places they had not yet heard of—Chu Lai, Khe Sanh, Hamburger Hill.

Today, a wall of black Bangalore granite rises out of the ground on the Washington, D.C., Mall like a 494-foot tombstone. The surface of the wall is meticulously inscribed with the names of 58,310 men and 8 women, names without stories or faces. War touched them with fire, and fetid swamps and steaming jungles swallowed them up. Brothers and sisters in arms, now rendered indifferent to all weather. Carl Riley turned down a college basketball scholarship to be among them.

Behind the letters that spell out the names of the honored, visitors see their own faces in the mirror-like wall, faces that show grief, awe, reverence.

This evening, as the comforting scent of cherry blossoms settles over the Mall, a final ray of sunlight filters through the trees and highlights the name of Carl Brendan Riley. On the ledge beneath his name, almost hidden in the growing shadows, is a yellowed photograph of Carl and Julie, smiling and holding hands. He wears a Marine uniform. Next to the photo is a worn square of blue cloth. On the cloth, there is a large red Q.

J. Allen Whitt is a Vietnam veteran who served three combat deployments to the Gulf of Tonkin aboard an aircraft carrier. He recently retired as a Professor Emeritus of Sociology. His novel *Notes From the Other Side of the Mountain: Love Confronts the Wounds of War* was a finalist in the 2013 New Mexico-Arizona Book Awards. One of his essays won first place in a national creative writing contest for veterans. His work has been published in *Military Experience and the Arts, Fifty-Something, Lyric, Cream City Review, Lowestoft Chronicle, Good Old Days, Reminisce, Front Porch, Westview, Concho Review,* and *Louisville Magazine.*

The Bunker

ROBERT SWANDBY

Honorable Mention

THE BRIGADE HAD BEEN CONDUCTING SEARCH AND destroy operations outside the base perimeter nearly every day since I arrived in early September. The farmers the troops brought us to interrogate said there were no Viet Cong in the area. I was a green 2nd lieutenant interrogation officer. In early December the detainees we questioned were scared and told us Viet Cong squads entered their village at night to recruit them, and told them if American troops captured them they would be killed. It was now mid-December, 1967 and something wasn't right. Each passing day the feeling in my gut grew stronger that we were going to be attacked. I just didn't know when.

The night before I arrived at the 3rd Brigade in September, the interrogation team of the 2nd Brigade, located further south near Can Tho, had taken a direct mortar hit. Hanh, my Vietnamese Army interpreter said, "Lieutenant, it was terrible. Everyone wounded. Shrapnel from roof, big as knives, deep cut everyone while they sleep. I came help. Everyone screaming and moaning. Robinson's lung punctured. It takes them two hours to get shrapnel out of Jones's butt." The picture in my mind of that carnage permeated every fiber of my being. I worried about my own team's safety.

The 3rd Brigade base was on Highway R on the south end of the provincial capital of Tan An, 30 miles south of Saigon. The entrance to the base was a turn directly off the highway. It had a long metal gate that was locked at night, but there was no manned guard station. The base was rectangular, a quarter block wide and a block long. It was enclosed by five-foot high barbed wire, and on top of that was another three feet of coiled razor concertina wire. My team slept and worked in a tin-roofed hooch outside, but adjacent to the brigade perimeter. We too were surrounded by barbed wire but did not have the added protection of concertina wire.

Our hooch was less than 20 yards from the brigade entrance gate. Any attack coming from the highway would hit us first. We appeared to be an afterthought in the base construction plan.

As I walked around the brigade on my first day, the heat of the midday sun and the fear I felt from Hanh's description of the previous night's attack caused me to sweat through my fatigue shirt. I felt nauseous. As I continued my tour, I observed something so obvious I had failed to notice it when I arrived. There was not a single bunker anyplace. I was dumbfounded. It was as if we were in a war zone, but there was no ongoing war. In that moment I decided I would find a way to protect my team.

I started looking around and discovered a pile of empty sandbags between our hooch and the brigade mess hall. I gathered my team and we went to grab the sandbags, one wheelbarrow full at a time. We started building our bunker 20 feet from the back of our hooch, close to the perimeter barbed wire. I had no idea what I was doing, but Fitz, my easy-going senior sergeant, had construction experience. "No sweat, Lieutenant, we can do this." he grinned as he flipped his wavy blond hair away from his glasses.

We got shovels and began filling the sandbags. We found some two-by-fours lying around and sawed them into short lengths to frame a firing port. I surveyed our handiwork the next morning. It was solid, even though it looked motley with mostly gray, but some green, sandbags.

We had four feet of sandbags stacked in the square shape of the bunker. Fitz was directing the framing of the firing port. Out of the corner of my eye I saw the crew-cut head and steel gray eyes of the executive officer striding through the brigade's steel gate into our tiny compound. In his usual brusque voice he shouted, "Lieutenant, colonel wants to see you immediately." Beads of sweat formed on my forehead and my stomach churned as I accompanied the major back to the colonel's spiffy white metal, air-conditioned trailer surrounded by a one-foot high plastic fence.

We entered the trailer. The colonel was sitting in a straight-backed chair near his desk. He was a fortyish six-footer with straight, combed back brown hair, square face, and brown eyes. His camouflage fatigues were pressed and jungle boots were spit shined. He appeared friendly as he rose to greet me, but then his face became set and serious. He offered me a straight-backed chair across from him. There was no small talk.

"Lieutenant, what are you doing with all those sandbags at your place?"

"Sir, we are building a bunker. Even though there have been no attacks since I've been here, I want to protect my men and myself if there is one." He looked at me thoughtfully for a few seconds, bowed his head and stared at the floor. That stare lasted a long time. I tried to remain calm but fidgeted in my chair and worried what he would say next.

When he finally raised his head, he looked me straight in the eyes, "I think that's not a bad idea, Lieutenant." He paused, again looked directly at me and with his serious face continued, "But you need to use just one color of sandbag—all green or all gray."

I replied, "Sir, I will do my best."

I left the meeting shaking my head. I knew there weren't enough sandbags to do all gray or all green so we just kept going. We reinforced the roof with steel planking and finished with two layers of sandbags on top so if we took a direct mortar hit the roof wouldn't turn into shrapnel.

Two days later, two Vietnamese flatbed trucks drove into the base loaded with sandbags. I grew curious. *What might be the purpose of all those sandbags?* I thought to myself. Shortly after the trucks parked a detail of soldiers started unloading the sandbags and another detail filled them with sand from a dump-truck-size pile. More soldiers came and hauled them off in wheelbarrows. Soon there were foundations of large bunkers appearing at each corner of the brigade perimeter. The frame of their gun ports suggested that each would house a .50 caliber machine gun. All over the base soldiers and officers were as busy as an ant colony building smaller bunkers near their hooches. I laughed to myself as I watched all this frantic activity with the realization that somehow the supply sergeant had managed to find two truckloads of gray sandbags. I was offered no sandbags, and I wasn't willing to wait to complete our bunker. Now it was finished and we were less vulnerable. We had a place to run for cover if attacked.

Christmas and New Year's came and went, and life remained routine. Fitz's tour was almost over and I needed to drive him back to division headquarters just north of Saigon. I had made the drive alone a few times before with no problem, but we heard intelligence of possible Viet Cong activity along Highway 4. A brigade convoy was leaving at 10 A.M. for Saigon. I decided it might be safer for us. We started off in my jeep near the rear of the convoy. After driving a few miles, we heard firing ahead. I looked at Fitz with my hands tight on the steering wheel so he wouldn't see them trembling, "What the hell do you think's going on?" I shouted to mask my fear.

As every vehicle came to a screeching halt, he replied, "I have no idea, Lieutenant, but I don't like it." Neither of us had been under fire before. In a few minutes a soldier, breathless from running down the convoy line, shouted "ambush, lead vehicle hit." We sat nervously in the jeep waiting for instructions. Minutes passed, then a quarter hour passed and there was no movement and no orders. We were squirming in our seats with no idea of what was happening ahead.

Just as I was thinking about turning around, Fitz turned to me and said, "Lieutenant, I would really prefer not going home in a body bag." That clinched it. I started the jeep, pulled out of the convoy, did a sharp U turn and sped back toward base. Out of the corner of my eye I could see Fitz's smile and his wavy blond hair blowing in the warm breeze. As we sped toward home he said, "Thanks, Lieutenant."

A few days later, I was sitting outside near the front of our hooch soaking up the quiet of my favorite time of the day. Twilight was giving way to a clear moonless night. The only sounds were the chirping of crickets and the swishing of the leaves of the coconut palms rubbing against each other in the gentle breeze. I was half asleep in my chair. Sharp staccato automatic rifle firing in short bursts startled me awake. I jumped out of my chair. It sounded far away. I thought maybe the Vietnamese Army compound across town was doing some late training. The firing got louder and more insistent. Most of my interrogation team were standing around our hooch talking. Then the firing came blasting at us and bullets whizzed over our heads. We scrambled over each other and dove head first into our bunker. My heart raced as I landed on top of the others. I could feel my body tensing as we bumped into each other and I smelled the sweat of fear. Quickly, we grabbed each other's shirts to get back on our feet to see what was happening.

Sam, my oldest sergeant, was a WWII Japanese-American veteran of small stature and jet-black hair. He started screaming in his high staccato voice. "Lieutenant, we're all going to die, we're going to die here." His screaming both angered and terrified me. We were on our feet now grabbing our M14 rifles. I whirled toward Sam and brought the back of my left hand up hard against his cheek. As he staggered back, nearly falling, I yelled, "God dammit, Sam, shut up." His hand came up to his face as he backed away in terror.

Next came the whoosh of rockets going over the top of our bunker and the loud cracks and explosions as they landed. They were quickly joined by the dull thump, thump, thump of mortar rounds marching toward us and exploding close. I saw muzzle flashes from the nearby corner bunker port as the brigade's sentry returned fire with his .50 caliber machine gun. Soon every soldier and officer joined the firing to ward off the attack. The constant cacophony of ear-shattering sounds and blinding light disoriented me. My team and I took turns firing our M14s on full automatic from our port, but we couldn't see anything. The smell of gunpowder was strong and smoke and dust blurred our vision.

The initial attack lasted an hour. Then there was a lull for nearly a half hour before we heard sporadic bursts of semi-automatic rifle fire and machine gun fire. The blackness and smoke made it impossible to assess how the brigade was faring. All of our attention was focused toward Tan An City. Then I remembered my bigger fear. The enemy could sneak up behind us from the south and blow the brigade gate. The cool night air made me shiver. I started crawling out of the bunker on my elbows and knees with my M14 held in my upturned palms to keep it from hitting the dirt. I crawled through our hooch, cursing at the pain the wood flooring caused my knees and elbows with each move forward. Sweat was running off my forehead into my eyes. I had to stop, remove my glasses and wipe my eyes with my shirtsleeve so that I could see into the dark hooch. As I reached the front entrance to the hooch, my teeth began to chatter from the cold sweat soaking my shirt all the way to my groin. I paused to consider whether to stand up to get a better view but decided that could be fatal. I crawled through the open door. It was a little lighter outside the hooch and I directed my eyes to the brigade entrance. I scanned up and down the road, but I saw no enemy movement. I rose to a crouch, spun around and ran back to the bunker.

The night dragged on and firing continued sporadically. We choked from all the smoke and dust in the air. I found a few minutes to check our status. My teeth were still chattering so I asked Fitz to call each man's name to see if we had any wounded. I also asked him to check our wire. In a few minutes he shouted, "no wounded, Sir," then shined a flashlight through the port along the length of our wire. "Wire intact, Sir."

The night was feeling colder and I began to think about how we would handle a second attack. Around 2 A.M. I heard the drone of a prop-driven plane in the distance. In no time it was circling and then I heard the ripping of large caliber bullets tearing up the ground so close I could see dust rise where they hit. Flares went up from the brigade and I saw the shadow figures of two enemy soldiers running outside our perimeter.

We learned later that the plane was "Puff the Magic Dragon," an AC-47 transport modified with three mini-guns, one at each door. Each mini could fire 100 rounds per second. After the Puff barrage, firing stopped and there was an eerie silence. I tried to let my body relax, but it refused. I grew shaky with fatigue wondering what morning would bring and whether there would be prisoners to interrogate. As night gave way to dawn, two infantry lieutenants came to our bunker and asked me to join them to reconnoiter outside the brigade wire. In the chill before sunrise, the acrid smell of gunpowder permeated the air and the dust from the firefight was settling close to the ground.

We started toward the southeast bunker but didn't see anything except torn up dirt and grass from the Puff attack. As we approached the bunker, I saw there was a one-foot hole blown through it. Sand was spilling out of the shredded sandbags around it. The taller of the two lieutenants turned to me and said, "You guys were damn lucky last night. The machine gunner was killed by a rocket, but an old sarge ran up and kept firing."

I started shaking again as I realized that we would have been penetrated if that bunker had been taken out. We continued to walk the wire toward the northeast bunker and turned the corner. A mess ahead stopped us in our tracks. Six enemy soldiers lay dead within yards of each other; a Viet Cong wearing only black shorts, sitting, legs out-stretched, slumped forward, shot in the back; a North Vietnamese Army regular in black uniform was on his back, right leg bent to the right at the shattered knee, left arm twisted behind his head, eyes wide with a look of total surprise, and an open, blood-filled mouth. The four others were in similar states of disarray. They were already stiff and wooden looking as if they had never been alive. The ground around each was blood soaked. They were all within yards of the brigade's north wire. Since they were all bunched close to the wire, I suspected they were a sapper team trained to blow barbed wire so the rest of the attackers could enter. After completing the perimeter check I returned to my team, which was rechecking our defenses.

Mid-morning the executive officer strode into our area. "Lieutenant, four prisoners were captured during the firefight. They're at the Army of Vietnam compound and you need to interrogate them as soon as possible and report to the colonel."

"Yes, Sir, I'm on it."

After lunch Fitz, Hanh, and I got into my jeep and headed for the compound on the north side of town. When we arrived, we were escorted into an open courtyard in the back of the compound surrounded by a stone wall. As we came through the compound door into the courtyard, four North Vietnamese prisoners sat clustered on the ground. They were blindfolded and handcuffed. The two Vietnamese Army soldiers guarding them prodded them with their rifles to stand as we approached. I asked the guards to remove the blindfold and cuffs of the one closest to us, which they did reluctantly. We escorted the soldier to the other side of the courtyard out of earshot from his comrades. He trembled and kept his eyes on the ground as he walked. I spoke to him softly, assured him we would not harm him, and offered him a cigarette. Hahn calmly translated my words and lit his cigarette, which began to put him at ease.

His name was Binh. I asked how he had gotten here and what was his unit and its mission. "I come from Tan Mai village, south of Hanoi. Liberation soldiers come to Tan Mai and demand all boys come to the village center. There are many of us, but they send younger boys home. They keep Bui, Minh, Duc and myself and say we are going on an important mission."

"What mission?"

"They say we are going with them on long march down Ho Chi Minh trail to liberate South Vietnam. Say goodbye to your family. We leave now. We walk long time at night to another village where there are many boys like us gathered – maybe two hundred. They come from many villages. They give us black uniforms, AK-47 rifles and Ho Chi Minh sandals."

"Binh, how old are you?" "I am fourteen."

"And your comrades?" "Duc is fourteen. Bui and Minh are fifteen."

"How long did it take you to reach Tan An?" "Not sure, maybe two months. Very long walk."

"And how was the march?" "It was very, very bad. We walk all night, get many bombs, many soldiers die."

"What did you eat?" "We get one small bowl of rice each day, usually moldy."

"What happened when you reached Tan An." "We get lost. We can't find meeting place with Viet Cong who will show us where to attack. We keep looking and two days later they find us. It was very bad. We had no time. We meet them late afternoon, attack soon after dark."

"Ah, now the convoy attack makes sense," I said to Fitz. "When I was trying to take you back to division the ambush on the convoy occurred two days before the full attack on the base. The convoy was likely a target of opportunity for the Viet Cong or the North Vietnamese who were trying to find each other."

We also interrogated Bui, Minh and Duc separately. Their stories matched Binh's. I looked at Hanh and Fitz and said, "What the hell is going on, they sent boys to attack us." Hanh ventured that the North Vietnamese Army was running out of adult soldiers.

The following night we were attacked again, but there were no rockets, mortars or machine guns, just rifle fire that was farther away. It appeared to be a probe to see if we were still vulnerable, or it could have been that there weren't many Viet Cong or North Vietnamese soldiers left after Puff had nailed them the previous night. I was distraught at the possibility of a third night of attacks. I was on edge and shaky. With no real sleep for two days I couldn't think clearly and a feeling of despair overtook me. I thought, *If they attack again let them kill me outright.*

As the sun rose on the third day, I'd grabbed a few hours of sleep before dawn. I lay on my cot, half-awake and began thinking about the terrified North Vietnamese boy soldiers, the lack of any bunkers when I arrived, and the insanity of shooting at people I'd never seen before. Fitz was waking up two cots away. It was time for another attempt to drive him to division for his trip home.

"We made it through, Fitz, all of us. Thanks for all your help with the bunker."

"No problem, Lieutenant."

"Fitz, I think I'll go home with you," I joked. Fitz grinned at me, "Sorry Sir, you have six months before you can go back to the world."

"Damn," I shot back.

Bob Swandby is a lover of poems, essays, memoirs and novels. He writes poems and memoirs and walks the Boise River every day with his dog Woody to stay connected to the land. He has done horse rescue work in New Mexico and volunteers with the Idaho Dog Alliance Project of Idaho (IDAPI) that takes Idaho Humane Society dogs to Idaho Correctional facilities for an eight-week intensive socialization and training program with selected inmates, so they can be adopted into the community.

Marching to a Different Drummer

Gordon Smith

Honorable Mention

THE OLD MAN SITTING BESIDE THE FOURTH OF JULY parade route struggled to his feet.

Three flags were leading the parade. He knew exactly where the "real" flag was, and he was ready. The other two dipped slightly, one on either side of it. No one in this country's history ever knowingly made our flag lower than any other.

The band blasted out "The Star-spangled Banner." Suddenly the two accompanying flags were a bit blurry because his eyes filled with tears. But the stars and stripes appeared to be as clear to him as they ever had been. He had honored the red, white and blue for many, many years.

He offered a shaky salute, standing at attention as best he could, leaning heavily on the padded crutch that helped to steady him. His salute would not have passed inspection for crispness back in boot camp so long ago. But now it was a real strain to shift his weight and balance against the half-empty sleeve and the vacant trouser leg, both on his left side.

Back when he was just a boy, his patriotic spirit was already causing some difficulty for his parents. It was at just such a parade as this that he was caught up in the fervor and he pleaded with them to sign for him so that he could enlist in the service. He was much too young, they told him. But all three knew that he would always be too young, in their eyes. He was their only child. The lure of ships and planes and tanks had pulled him toward America's second try at fighting a "war to end all wars," as President Wilson had termed the first. There was something magnetic about the theme of making the world safe for democracy, even though he understood very little about what was involved, or what freedom really meant. On this point he was very much like many other Americans who took their liberty for granted. Because his parents and their parents had always been free, they did not find it necessary to discuss the concept with their son.

He just knew that when the horns blasted out the martial airs, and the drums marked cadence for those synchronized marching feet, and the men and women looked so smart in their uniforms, carrying rifles, arms swinging, giving an "eyes right" as they passed the commander, he had to be right in the middle in his mind, marching with them to whatever lay ahead. He was too young to realize that something serious was going on. But his spirit of patriotism had been born then and there.

His parents gave in. The need for patriots was great. America had been attacked. The world was in a mess. With heavy heart, they signed for him to enlist.

The long arduous days of training, of conditioning, of lectures about how a soldier should conduct himself on the battlefield without fear, had prepared him as well as was possible for the chaos that faced him on the beach at Normandy. He was not a leader, with bars to mark his rank. But he was a follower, and he did as he was commanded, and he did it well. He was one of thousands of heroes who did their duty without seeking glory or reward. Battles require more followers than leaders. Sometimes advancing, sometimes retreating, sometimes just digging in, as a lowly foot soldier he thought often of the words of Milton: "They also serve who only stand and wait."

It has been said that a soldier never hears the bullet that changes his life forever. But somewhere in the dim recesses of his mind he did remember the high-pitched whine of the shell that almost ended his days on earth. The last that he knew was the lifting of his body toward the heavens by the force of the blast. After that, he felt nothing for weeks. He awoke in an ocean of white sterility in the camp hospital. Gradually he became conscious of his surroundings. He heard the moans and curses and cries of his comrades. He tried to pull himself up, out of the bed, to see who was around him. But half of his body would not respond, and searing pain pushed him back down into oblivion.

Over the weeks of rehabilitation and learning how to perform normal tasks with only part of his humanity intact and functioning, he grew stronger. But in his mind he had the depressing feeling that he had let his buddies down. They were out there somewhere, fighting, dying. And he could not help them.

Even now, after many years, at another Independence Day parade, he felt bad that he could not be right in the middle of it, marching with fellow soldiers, their eyes focused on that imaginary line ahead where the enemy waited, ears attuned to the stirring strains that kept their feet in step: "O say, can you see. . . ." Yes, he could see it! He saw that glorious banner in his dreams. He felt the tug of it at his heart, the warmness of its colorful silk, the proud emblem of a free nation that rose to the challenge of enabling the world's peoples to enjoy the fruits of liberty and justice.

Then one day his friends and family gathered around the flag-draped brown box that held the earthly proof that this man was a patriot. It seemed that he wore the uniform proudly in death, the medals gleaming, the crisp stripes on the sleeves telling how hard and faithfully he had labored. In accordance with his final wishes, they had pinned up the sleeve and the trouser leg, not trying to hide the truth of his sacrifice, but deliberately reminding viewers that here was a patriot who had not just talked about liberty, who had not just marched to the drums of freedom, who had not just sung songs about flags and banners, but who had put his manhood on the line for what he believed.

In closing the service at the grave, just before the playing of "Taps," the chaplain cited the words of Adlai Stevenson: "What do we mean by patriotism in the context of our times? A patriotism that puts country ahead of self; a patriotism which is not short, frenzied outbursts of emotion." Then the padre added, "Patriotism demands the best that we have, expects more than we thought we could give, and sometimes takes it all."

As the flag was removed from the coffin, folded and presented to his family, the people in attendance thought that they heard in the distance the sound of a marching company of soldiers, the drum beating out the cadence to keep them together, in step, on their way to protect their country.

And they could see, as in a vision, this patriot who, once again, with a whole body, was in step, marching to a different drummer.

Gordon Smith is a retired public school science teacher living in Hot Springs, Arkansas, with his wife, Carol, who is also a retired public school teacher. They both enjoy writing, with Gordon preferring poetry, short stories and essays, and Carol liking essays and travel articles.

I, The Ensign

SUSAN LINDSLEY

Honorable Mention

IN HIGH SCHOOL, SHE HAD WATCHED THE WOMEN MARCH across her hometown college campus, the tromp of their shoes sounding a rhythm that beat with her heart. These women served with as much pride as the men who served aboard ships and in the army to free Europe.

The Second World War was over, but the WAVES, the Women's Auxiliary Volunteer Emergency Service, was still operational. She wanted to be a part of it, to join these women she so admired.

Her brother had joined the Navy and often spoke of the camaraderie. Maybe, she thought, it would be the same in the women's portion of the Navy. A farm girl, she had never felt at ease among the city girls in college. When a WAVES officer came to her college to recruit officer candidates, she was weeks from graduation. She jumped at the chance to join.

She left home with the confidence of a World Series winning pitcher. But when she arrived at the Officer Candidate School and discovered all the other students were well versed in military matters, she felt left out. Loneliness and fear of greater loneliness seeped into her. How could she belong to this group when all she knew about the Navy was how much she loved the marching women in her home town, when the nine other students were already military? Two were enlisted WAVES, one was an army WACS sergeant and one an enlisted WACS. And five were WAVES chiefs, top rank for a naval noncommissioned officer. She alone had never been in uniform.

She also had never been anywhere, except to college in her home town, where she earned a summa cum laude diploma in 1951. But she had never been gregarious, had never been able to build friendships. She wondered why she had thought joining the WAVES would give her something to belong to. She did not fit in with the other women—all older, all brimming with self-confidence and all experienced in life and in the military. They drank and smoked and often cussed. She took up smoking, but when she tried alcohol, the fire in her mouth deterred her.

Their interest in her frightened her until she realized they were trying to offer friendship and support. But when one praised her high shine on her marching brogans within hearing of the drill instructor, the lieutenant gave her a demerit for shoes not shined. She began to doubt their friendship was real—perhaps they just felt sorry for her. Or maybe they didn't like the idea of an outsider being in their officer-candidate class.

She loved the drilling and the marching. Loved the military classes where they studied outlines of the planes, both American and the now-feared Soviet jets, loved identifying the outline of ships. As she had done in college, she excelled in her classes.

Graduation and commissioning finally came, along with orders. She was going to the JAX naval station, heart of the Jacksonville Naval Base. The rest of the class envied her for getting the prize billet.

She was assigned to the Information and Education Office, and on her second day, she and the chief in the office were given the unenviable task of disposing of the service-wide examination booklets used the week before. Since the exams were classified, each booklet bore an identification number; each had to be located and checked off a master list. The ensign and chief spent two days comparing numbers on the booklets to numbers on the list. They stopped only for coffee and lunch.

One was missing. They rechecked. Same booklet was still missing. The ensign went to her supervising officer, and the lieutenant joined them to recheck.

After four days, the missing exam had not been found.

The lieutenant told her the Naval Station had never lost a classified document and he would discuss the matter with the executive officer.

While he was gone, she turned to the chief. She remembered all the comments her chief classmates had made about the 90-day wonders who didn't know beans about the military after their stint in OCS. "What do you think about the burn report, Chief?"

"We're going to be ordered to sign it as burned. I think we shouldn't sign it, Ma'am. That would be lying under penalty of perjury. If the exam shows up somewhere, we'd both be in serious trouble."

She nodded. "We won't be in trouble for disobeying an order to sign it?"

"No, Ma'am. That would be an illegal order."

The lieutenant returned, and as the chief predicted, he came with the orders to burn the exams and report that all were burned.

"I'm sorry, Sir, but I cannot sign off that I burned something when I didn't."

Standing behind her, the chief dittoed her comment.

"Okay," the lieutenant said. "I'll go with you, Ensign, and we'll burn the documents and I'll sign off and get the executive officer to co-sign."

The ensign was relieved. They loaded the boxes into the back of a Navy station wagon and headed for the burn pile. Two other naval officers were there, burning flight jackets.

"Wow," the ensign said. "What's wrong with those jackets?"

"Probably just a zipper off track."

"Why burn them?"

"Well, it's regulations. They're too expensive to just let the pilots take them home. People would be messing up zippers all the time just to get a free jacket."

The ensign shook her head. "Doesn't make sense to me. I don't see why they don't just get them fixed."

They quieted and began to dump the boxes of papers onto the fire. The lieutenant picked up a long rake leaning against the fence by the gate and used it to stir the papers. Two hours of breathing smoke and fighting flying ashes, and the project was over. Uniforms would have to go to the cleaners to get rid of the smell.

The lieutenant left with the burn report to go to the station's executive office.

He returned two hours later. "Did you get it signed, Sir?" she asked.

He nodded. "Yes. But I had to agree with you. I couldn't sign it either. The executive officer and the station commander signed it. But not a word to anyone, you understand?"

"Yes, Sir," she replied.

Three weeks later, she was given guard duty at the entrance to a top-secret meeting. Her assignment came with written orders and with an identification card. Only individuals with such a card were to be admitted.

What if somebody tries to get by me? What if somebody doesn't have a card and insists on getting in and is a senior officer?

She arrived an hour early at the meeting room and walked through it. Another entrance was unlocked. She checked the door, but there was no way to prevent anyone inside from letting someone enter through that door. She went back to the front door, where her assistant, a chief quartermaster, waited.

She had never met him, but he oozed the same confidence she had seen in her classmates. "Chief," she said. "I need your advice. The door across the way can be opened from the inside. What's best to do?"

"Ma'am, I can guard it if you want. Or get another petty officer."

"Don't you think the officers would be more inclined to leave the door alone if you are there rather than even a third class?"

The chief nodded and she realized he suppressed a smile as if trying to hide that he knew her thoughts. "Yes, Ma'am."

"Right. Okay, Chief, I'll leave that door up to you. I'll tend to this one."

The chief nodded, "Yes, Ma'am," and strode into the room to the other entrance. There he stood at parade rest in front of the door.

Ten minutes later, officers began to arrive. She stood to one side and asked each for his entrance permit. "Damn if I didn't leave it in my office," a commander said.

What would Ginny Jackson have done? She had the gumption to tell a captain she was not a steward's mate—it wasn't her job to serve food and drink—and she refused to get him a cup of coffee. I'll have to do what she would do. Not let him in.

"Sorry, Sir, but my orders state if you have no pass I am not to allow you to enter."

She felt sweat roll down her back. These brown-shoe Navy fly boys all wore summer browns and here she was in dress blues. She hoped her face wasn't sweating as much as her back and armpits.

The commander looked her up and down. Here was a shave tail girl, not more than twenty-two, telling him what to do. "Watchya gonna do, lady? Lock me up?"

"No, Sir," she stated and stepped between him and the door. Her insides trembled and she hoped her voice didn't. "But I will stand here until you get your pass. I do have orders. Sir."

The commander shook his head, muttered something about upstart women, turned and left.

Others drifted up, showed their ID and entered.

Ten minutes later, the commander returned, showed her his pass, and grinned. His tone was more polite than earlier. "May I enter now, Ensign?"

She smiled. "Certainly, Sir."

An admiral approached, in deep conversation with a captain. She recognized both. The captain was commanding officer of the air station. The admiral was commanding officer of the naval base.

They ignored her as they approached the doorway.

"Sir?" she stated and moved in front of the two senior officers.

"What?" the admiral said.

"I need to see your pass, Sir."

The admiral smiled. "I don't need a pass. It's my meeting."

Dear God, what do I do? If I let him in I'm disobeying orders. If I don't I'll be locked up for disobeying orders. But I can't let them in. If I do he could court martial me. But if I don't, he could.

"Sir, I'm sorry, but I can't let you in. I have written orders. No one is to enter without a pass signed by you, Sir. Those are your orders."

"That's right. But I sign the pass."

"I know, Sir. But I can't let you enter."

The captain spoke. "Ensign, he is your commanding officer. My commanding officer. You will stand down and let us enter."

"I'm sorry, Sir. I cannot." She tried to keep her eyes open and to meet his stare. Her stomach knotted. She feared she might throw up.

She stood mid-door, at parade rest, and blocked the entryway.

The admiral took a deep breath and exhaled. "Come on, Tom. We got no choice. We got ourselves one hell of a security-minded officer here. Let's go to the office and I'll write us both up a pass."

The two men started away. The ensign wobbled to the side of the door and leaned against the jamb. The admiral stopped, turned and said, "I've never had a junior office tell me what to do before. What you did took courage. And you did right."

When the meeting ended, the chief approached the ensign. "Ma'am, everybody at the meeting heard what you did. It took guts. I'm proud to have been your backup today."

Bareheaded, he violated naval protocol about saluting when inside and uncovered. He snapped to attention and saluted her.

She grinned and returned the honor.

Three days later, the base commander called to tell her he was transferring her to the Judge Advocate General's school for naval attorneys. "We need more like you," he said and ended the call.

Susan Lindsley has published in local, state and national publications. She has 12 published books, including poetry, biographies, fiction and memoir. Her work has won numerous awards from local, regional, national and international organizations. She also serves on a committee of judges for literary contests.

Surveillance

GERED BEEBE

Recognized

OFF THE BAJA CALIFORNIA COAST: SUMMER 1990. UNDER the waves swam a shadow, slow for now and large, but inherently fast and dangerous.

Inside the shadow lived a community. All male, at least for the foreseeable future, each sometimes had to remind himself—I volunteered for this. Nuclear submarine duty was not for everyone and was not an acquired taste. Each man either coped with it—or did not. Throughout this fast-attack submarine, inhabitants carried out their many duties. Amid gauges, colored lights, varied meters, and instruments, life prevailed.

The Control Room served as nerve center for this complex milieu of men and machines. This vital space had its own group of select watch-standers. Leader of this team, stationed on a raised dais stood the officer of the deck, often simply abbreviated as OOD. He was a lieutenant (junior grade) who had only recently earned his qualified submariner Dolphins badge. Twin periscopes, fully housed in their wells while running deep, could provide occasional windows to the outside.

Adjacent spaces housed other specialized watch-standers. Among these, sound detection and analysis was crucial. Like most denizens of the deep, the submarine was visually blind. Radar would not work. Electronic counter-measures had no signals to detect, much less to analyze. Radio was restricted to passive reception and only for powerful, low-frequency transmissions that could reach down this far. Sonar, the science and art of underwater sound, was king.

The OOD spoke through the tactical intercom, “Sonar, what contacts?”

“None close, Sir,” the reply filtered back. “Safe in our SO-CAL Op-Areas, the Berlin Wall has fallen, we reign supreme.”

“Just give me the contacts, Sonar.”

“Aye, Sir,” Sonar seemed to suppress a yawn. “None seem like combatants. None come from the now-defunct Soviet Bloc and none from the Chinese of either persuasion. Nor from anybody else America doesn’t happen to like this month.”

The watch team rippled with good-humored fun.

“Cut the crap, Sonar. What’s the nearest one?”

Sonar came back again, “Bearing north, northwest; drawing left. Sounds like a single screw making about 30 rpm; probably a large merchant out of San Diego. Give me a few, I can run it through the analyzer. Give you a short list of which ship it actually is.”

The OOD’s finger hovered near the intercom key. He finally responded, “Thanks, but no thanks, Sonar. Keep alert for anything unusual. We’re coming up to periscope depth soon.”

Sonar managed an affirmative reply.

Inside, the ship played its own harmony of operating equipment. Mostly, the crew knew the surge and sigh of high-pressure hydraulic fluid. The sub operated with the aid of hydraulic-powered control surfaces: bow planes, stern planes, and the two-piece rudder. While submerged the submarine required constant attention to maintain its depth—a problem not found with surface vessels. And casualties might occur without warning. Stern planes jammed at full dive and high speed could stand the sub on its nose and send it careening toward crushing depths. This was also not a problem with surface ships.

Whirring of ventilation fans added their whispered undertones. Many other devices contributed their hums, gentle clicks, and mellow annunciations. The quiet symphony ran on. Work carried on. Readings were taken then duly recorded. Checks of innumerable conditions were carried out, brief adjustments got done, status of all operating systems monitored to their last increment.

The OOD verified his Day Orders; he announced to the Control team.

"The Old Man's coming up for periscope depth soon. Let's show what a group of professionals we truly are."

At mid-afternoon they were to come to shallow cruising depth. This would keep the top of the submarine's high-strength steel, dorsal fin sail well below the keel of any surface vessel. Such collisions were rare, but the sail could tear through a surface ship's thin hull. Consequences would be dramatic, including injury and even death. And career-ending for any sub captain.

"Sonar, Conn, we're coming right. Check baffles and sweep around for any contacts," the OOD knew the stern view was never clear. Only occasional course changes would allow a glimpse behind by sonar. To be stealthy you must not let someone else practice stealth upon you. "Aye, Sir," came the reply.

At the designated time the undersea warship glided up to its new designated depth. The gentle up-angle was barely noticeable. The OOD checked various indicators; then pressed an intercom key. "We're ready for periscope depth, Captain. No contacts and ship's heading is 180."

A brief affirmative came back. The OOD knew the ship's boss was a low-key guy, but one who understood the importance of each event. Transit up to periscope depth was one of those. During that upward interval the submarine had few means of detecting a hazard. Everyone also knew, quiet or not, the captain was not one you wanted to piss off.

The captain arrived. He scanned key instruments and noted the intensity of the watch-standers. He stayed on the Control Room floor and issued his order, "Officer of the Deck, raise the ECM scope and bring the ship to periscope depth."

The young OOD suppressed his initial surprise. The CO was letting him do it. Well, a first time for everything.

"Aye, aye, Sir," the OOD pulled on the scope control ring. Working against sea pressure, the scope slowly lifted. As soon as the eyepiece rose from its well, the OOD crouched, dropped the handles, and spun to see in all directions underwater. Simultaneously he ordered, “Diving Chief, bring us to periscope depth.”

The seawater was alive with plankton and associated biologics. The Sonar speaker chirped with distant porpoises. Vision was murky. Taking aim forward, the OOD concentrated his view ahead.

Suddenly, through the blur, a shape appeared.

The OOD yanked on the scope control and sounded the Collision Alarm. “Emergency deep! Full down planes!”

The wailing siren screeched out its message. Crewmembers automatically slammed shut hatches and air duct dampers throughout the ship. In control, the periscope handles struck the well edge and snapped back into place as its glistening shaft plummeted down. Not perfect procedure, but the scope’s design allowed for it.

“What in hell!” The captain all but leaped to the raised level.

“Something up there, Skipper. Maybe a small boat, but couldn’t tell.”

The submarine settled back into friendly depths.

Numerous reports came back in response. Every station reported watertight security and no damage.

Despite the incident, the captain was somewhat satisfied. Overall, his crew just now demonstrated their training. He was particularly pleased that his new OOD brought down the periscope so quickly. A recent story told of a sub that had struck its scope on something, which then peened-over like a giant 10-penny nail.

By now the executive officer (XO) and operations officer (Ops) had joined the Conn Center team. They and the captain held a brief conference. At the end, the captain picked up the 1-MC General Announcing hand mic.

“All hands, this is the Captain. We had a close call topside. We’re going to withdraw a bit, then find out what’s up there. Now secure from collision.”

They went about a mile south. The Conn Center prepared for another assent. This time the captain rode the periscope up himself. He did the customary searches, both underwater and when the scope broke the surface. A quick scan showed all clear and then he concentrated on their contact, bearing north.

Pretty as a picture, the sailboat looked like a schooner rig and was maybe a 50-footer or larger. Whatever its make or size, the thing reeked of money. The captain conferred again, "XO, Ops, we're on independent operations, so let's be independent. We have a target of opportunity."

"Roger, Captain," the operations officer agreed. He took the 1-MC himself, "Now set the special tracking detail."

Tracking could cover a multitude of operations within the rubric of special. This time the sub would do an under-the-hull surveillance. Additional watch-standers arrived to augment the Conn group. Each took his place for the observations and recordings.

A key device was the portable periscope camera. The Interior Communications technician was needed for set-up. As an IC-runner during normal cruising, he was reasonably good; but as cameraman, not so hot. Some settings required knowledge of exposure and field of focus. The long umbilical cord, which rode with the camera into the periscope well, needed careful handling, too.

The submarine aimed for its target. Lowering the periscope below the surface between sightings was *de rigueur*. Slow speed was essential, too—no rooster tail wave that might give away the ship's position. Mr. All-Thumbs IC-runner could not focus the camera and maintain image depth at the same time. The captain looked impatient. The OOD reached past the technician and made the adjustment. Good. Now the Conn TV monitor and others in the ship showed clearly anything the periscope saw.

"Make sure they haven't deployed a sea anchor," the captain ordered a deeper depth. A mini-parachute could keep a small vessel in place on the open sea. But it could also play hell on a submarine mast if entangled; after that, so much for non-detection. His look-around was quick—none.

The underside examination went routine. No unusual appurtenance; the fancy sailing vessel looked like so many others from down here. Owners kept their hulls clean.

"Let's check topside."

They withdraw to a suitable distance. In a position that would bring the afternoon sun behind them, they rose a bit, and he aimed the periscope. There was movement on deck.

"And, hello . . ." the captain said.

A man and a woman had emerged from the yacht's low cabin. The camera caught their next actions in detail. First, they engaged in a passionate embrace. Then they spread a blanket atop the cabin roof. Then they deliberately took off their few clothing items. The young woman's figure was perfect.

The captain's eye had not left the periscope, *"Farewell and adieu, to you fair Spanish…"* the crooning lyrics trailed away. He dipped the scope below the waves.

A low collective groan emerged as the TV monitor showed only water. After a brief, but sufficient time, the captain again raised the periscope.

By now the two passionate yachtspersons had stretched onto their blanket.

"Ah, gentlemen, we have a natural phenomenon, the dance of love," the captain briefly turned away from the eyepiece. "And I don't mean the *Bossa Nova* either."

A few chuckles circulated. As the image again crept below water, another sigh filled the room. Drumming his fingers briefly on a railing, the captain issued his next pronouncement, "But seems this target has appropriate interest. We are obliged therefore to conduct a thorough investigation."

This brought murmurs of joy and a few whispered comments. The IC-runner, whose skills seemed limited at times, was now fully capable of connecting the remote monitors, including the one in the crew's galley. Word spread instantaneously. Rapt attention ensued as the captain maneuvered for new angles of view.

Events atop the yacht continued to unfold. Energy exuded without fail; variations and permutations seemingly without end. The ardent lovers never broke stride. Further evidence of their perfect health got vigorously displayed.

The XO took the scope and contributed his observation, "Stamina like that; need to find out what this guy eats."

"He doesn't look that old," a voice noted. "And she sure doesn't," someone else observed. Most felt tacit assurance that rich types lived in a world all their own. A world open only to them; a world that brooked few visitors, or so they thought.

"Don't suppose they bothered to check the Notice-to-Mariners.

They're not supposed to be here at all," the captain mused aloud as he viewed the monitor. By now the OOD had taken his turn at the camera-equipped periscope. "Looks like they've reached a stopping point." The pair now lay side-by-side in the afternoon sun. No other yacht sailors had ever appeared.

"Think we can call it quits, too." The captain signaled things were coming to an end. Some murmurings of dismay rippled around the Conn. The XO quipped, "Guess the only hot wash-up for this exercise will be those two. Sweaty." Dismay morphed into low-order mirth.

With characteristic stealth the undersea warship disengaged its thorough, yet life-affirming sighting. The special tracking detail was secured. Ship's course to the south was resumed. Steps were taken to ensure the Recording tape was preserved. Other crew who could not get to a monitor during the special action sequence would get their chance.

Later, the Conn Station team and OOD along with all other watch-standers had reported their reliefs. As required, the off-going OOD conducted a bow-to-stern, compartment-by-compartment survey. More than one thumbs-up sign of approval was received. When done, he knocked and entered the commanding officer's stateroom.

Inside, the captain and XO were conferring. "Watch has been relieved, Skipper," the young officer stated. He shut the door behind him.

"So that sequence was not exactly what they teach in sub school," the captain began. His off-going OOD shuffled a bit and smiled. "Good work on keeping our valuable government periscope intact. Some day I hear they're going to get rid of them. Use only telescoping camera masts with flex cabling sealed into the hull. Maybe they'll even work. So aside from all that, how did your watch go?"

The lieutenant (junior grade) paused a moment, then, "I have a smart-ass sonar operator and an IC tech with trouble finding his ass. Otherwise, all was fine, Skipper." The three shared a laugh.

"We are out here training, incidents notwithstanding. Bugs will get ironed out. So go get some chow."

After their junior officer left, the captain continued, "Before too long, impose some internal quality control. Showing that tape is okay, but it will never leave this ship. Erase it if necessary."

"Understand, Sir. And it seems our new guy has what it takes," XO offered.

"My thoughts, too," the captain stroked his chin. "Wonder what he'll say when he learns what we're really going to do."

Gered Beeby, a graduate of the U.S. Naval Academy at Annapolis, began his career as a nuclear submarine officer. Later he joined the Naval Reserve as an engineering duty officer (EDO) and eventually retired with the rank of captain. A licensed professional engineer in California, he participated in a variety of engineering and construction management assignments. He has written a novel, short fiction, essays, and screenplays. He served as president (2003) of the San Diego Writers and Editors Guild and currently serves on its board of directors.

Maggie Takes the Constellation

MARGUERITE F. MCDOLE

Recognized

I CHOSE A VERY STYLISH BUT IMPRACTICAL OUTFIT FOR my 19-hour flight to Frankfurt, Germany, as I dressed at the hotel in New York that May of 1953. It was a pink silk, polka-dot dress that I had purchased specifically for my arrival; a two-piece with a sleeveless top and a knee-length skirt with knife pleats. My shoes were dressy summer sandals, and my hair was in the latest Audrey Hepburn style. I was 22 and leaving on the most adventurous journey of my life.

My six-month-old daughter and I were on our way to Wiesbaden, Germany, to join my husband, Bob, a staff sergeant in the U.S. Air Force stationed there during the American occupation. I promised that I would join him in Wiesbaden for the last six months of his tour of duty and I kept this promise. I was excited and a little out of breath, since we were late arriving at the airport from our hotel in Manhattan where we had stayed the night before. The TWA agent had been paging me from the gate.

The stewardess helped with our luggage as I climbed the steps to board the TWA Lockheed Constellation, and guided us to a seat near the rear of the plane. The crew members were all young and attractive, dressed in their jaunty skirts, jackets and high heels. When we were seated, I was relieved that my seatmate for the long trip was a friendly, helpful woman.

The Constellation gathered speed as the captain taxied down the runway. As we climbed to our cruising altitude of 20,000 feet, I could see the Manhattan skyline below. I held my daughter Lauri tight and said to myself, "Bob is waiting for us in Frankfurt—I know we'll have a wonderful time." I breathed a sigh of relief and let the worries and stress of the past year evaporate.

During the flight, my seatmate offered to hold my daughter when I had to leave my place for a few minutes. It was cool on the plane and I wished I had worn a more comfortable outfit. After we were served sandwiches and a drink, I settled back in my seat and gave my daughter a bottle of milk. Several hours into the flight, we landed at Gander, Newfoundland, in pea soup fog. We had a drink and a bite to eat while the Constellation was being refueled in preparation for our long flight across the Atlantic to Frankfurt.

Bob and I were married in the Chapel at Lowry Air Force Base in Denver, Colorado, in 1952 with my family and a few close friends in attendance. My husband enlisted in the Air Force during the Korean War and was stationed in Denver for basic training. Soon after, he was deployed to USAF European Headquarters in Wiesbaden, Germany, where he would serve as his unit's historian.

But there was another major role that Bob would take on within his unit. When commanding officers found out that he was a top-notch tennis player who held city and state titles in Indiana, they enthusiastically recruited him to put together a championship Air Force Tennis Team, for which he would go on to play #1 singles and doubles at the Wiesbaden Tennis and Hockey Club and in matches around the world.

Because Bob had enlisted in the Air Force, our benefits did not include an officer's military housing, so we would be living on the economy. This meant renting our own apartment, and shopping at the local markets. A round-trip airplane ticket from New York to Frankfurt was $1,000, and I had to save this amount in a short time. After this initial expenditure, we would be able to live well, since the value of the German mark was about 25 cents.

I applied for a position at the University of Notre Dame to earn money to pay for my ticket. I had worked there previously and the campus with The Basilica of the Sacred Heart, the ivy-covered Grotto, and the lake where we hiked made for a beautiful setting in which to work. The Administration Building with the Golden Dome was in the Main Quad. This is where I met Dr. E.K. Francis, prior director of the Sociological Institute at the University of Munich. He was at Notre Dame completing research for his book about the Mennonites of Manitoba, and I was hired to transcribe and type his notes.

Dr. Francis had an outgoing personality with a sparkle in his dark brown eyes that indicated his intelligence. As we worked together, he revealed his personal history and the circumstances under which he was forced to leave Austria.

He was part of a group of elite scientists, sociologists and writers from Germany and Austria who were forced to go into hiding because they wrote and spoke out against the Nazi regime. Knowing his life was in danger, he had fled Austria, temporarily leaving his family behind, and immigrated to Canada, where he taught at a women's academy. After the war, he secured a teaching position at the University of Notre Dame and brought his family to the U.S.

After working together for a few weeks, we shared stories about our families and got to know each other better. Dr. Francis knew that I was at a crossroads in my life and wanted to help me. I told him about my husband who was serving in Germany and my plans to join him for the remainder of his tour of duty. He agreed that this was a rare opportunity and advised me to visit all the famous German museums; he also suggested the best way to cross the Atlantic was by ship. I had a different plan. Transatlantic passenger air travel was fairly new and this was something I looked forward to.

After assisting him for four months, my temporary assignment was finished, but I felt a tinge of regret when we said goodbye. My last week working together, he invited me to his home for a traditional German meal, and to meet his wife and young son. The professor also presented me with a corsage as a bon voyage.

I was pleased to book a flight on the "Connie." Overnight, after they had dimmed the lights, I managed to catch a couple hours of sleep. Early in the morning, the stewardess brought us orange juice, breakfast rolls, and hot coffee. When the captain announced our descent, I pulled out my compact to check my hair and makeup.

It had been a safe journey and I was overjoyed when we landed. My husband, handsome in his dress blues, was waiting at the bottom of the steps, a worried look on his face. We were the last of the 64 passengers to emerge, since we were seated in the rear of the plane. It was a happy reunion—we had been separated for months and he would hold our daughter for the first time. It was a warm May morning, and I relaxed as I walked out into the balmy mountain air.

Our driver took us from the airport to where we would be staying in Wiesbaden. My husband had rented an apartment in a German home, but I didn't know any details about the family. Later I learned Herr Von Jagow was a retired colonel who had served in the German Army during WWI, and his son Bally had been a tank commander for the Army during WWII. Driving through the town to their home, I could see neighboring houses bombed by the English and Americans toward the end of the war. The primary targets had been munitions factories and railroad stations, but some homes were destroyed. Their house was on a mountainside with a breathtaking view of the city. As we approached, I could hear music from an open window on the third floor, a tenor practicing an aria.

I smiled when I was introduced to Frau Von Jagow by my husband. I wanted to make a good impression since we would be living with them for six months. She was middle aged and matronly with a round face, pink cheeks and gray hair. She spoke German, French, and English fluently and translated English for her husband.

My first morning there, Bob put his arm around me, saying; "Maggie, I want you to have a nice vacation and enjoy yourself while we're here. The family has a neighbor with a teenage daughter who will babysit. You'll be able to go to the Wiesbaden Tennis Club and relax; we're guest members and we can use the club and pool.

"They call me the Tennis Boss," he joked. "When they found out I was South Bend City Champion and ranked in Indiana, they asked me to help organize the Air Force team for the Wiesbaden post. I'll be playing in a lot of tournaments and we can all go together. One will be in Berchtesgaden; we'll have a car and driver and stay in a very nice hotel there for the weekend." I jumped up and hugged him. I was looking forward to seeing his team compete.

With his slight build, boyish face, blond hair and blue eyes, I found it impossible to picture our host Bally in his German Army uniform. A tank driver during the war, he seemed to have adjusted to civilian life and now traversed the city on his motorbike. During our brief conversations, we avoided discussing the war.

We had a comfortable, private suite of rooms on the second floor of their three-story home in the mountains, and our surroundings, especially during the summer and fall, could not have been more spectacular. One could tell that the home had been palatial in the past. It was somewhat worn, although comfortable and clean. Their maid, Gisela, came once a week to scrub the wooden floors and perform other tasks. She also took care of my laundry for which we paid her, ironing my cotton dresses with a flatiron heated on the stove.

Our rooms had high ceilings, oversized furniture, and tapestries and paintings adorning the walls. The warm June mornings were perfect for having our breakfast at the small table on the balcony off the living room, with a lovely view of the mountains. We had breakfast there every morning: coffee, usually eggs and toast, and a delicious preserve with the toast. Eggs, especially, were fresh and very good. I bought them every day at the market, just three or four since they were scarce. Lauri liked them, and they were a healthy source of protein since there was no baby food available.

Frau Von Jagow helped me become familiar with Wiesbaden and its shops and parks. The colonel was a retired army officer, but it was obvious that his wife was in charge of the household, and she made clear our obligation as tenants; for instance, I was told there were to be no dishes left in the sink overnight.

After Bob's leave had ended and he returned to work, I settled into a daily routine. In the morning, I made a list and walked to the market pushing my daughter in a stroller. In the afternoon, we went to the park where daisies and pansies were in bloom. On warm July afternoons, I went to the tennis club where I swam and had a Coke and cookies by the pool. Our 14-year-old neighbor Elsbeth, who was cheerful and eager to please, came to babysit. She was fluent in English and preferred my English translation of her name, "Elizabeth."

Wiesbaden was rich with history. Known as a resort city, it was home to 300 millionaires before the war. Situated on the Northern Bank of the Rhine River, it is one of the oldest spa towns in Europe, its name translating to "meadow baths." The area was famous for its recreation pools for bathing, and for gambling. Some well-known visitors to the springs had included Wolfgang von Goethe, Fyodor Dostoevsky, Richard Wagner and Johannes Brahms.

The price we paid for lodging was very reasonable due to the favorable exchange rate. From our purchases at the American PX we were able to give the family occasional gifts of coffee, Coca-Cola, and cigarettes, items that were all in short supply. They loved Coke, drinking it from a small glass and savoring it much like wine. When Von Jagow saw us preparing a typical evening meal of roast beef and vegetables, he remarked to his wife that the amount of meat we ate at one meal would feed a German family for a week.

Bob took me out for dinner in mid-July to celebrate my 23rd birthday. I wore a blue cotton sundress with matching bolero jacket, a three-strand pearl necklace, and Shalimar perfume, his birthday present to me. We walked to one of the many fine restaurants in town, where we drank Moselle wine, with its green apple and lightly mineral flavor, and I tried their specialty of hard-boiled eggs with caviar for the first time.

I was absorbing the language and customs as quickly as possible since I was on my own while my husband was working. I soon found my favorite shops for pastries, fruits and vegetables, and meat at the local butcher shop. We ate only fresh fruits and vegetables since there were very few canned goods available. Before leaving for my daily shopping, I went over the list with Frau Von Jagow, asking her how to say, "Do you have eggs, milk and bread?" which translated to, "Haben sie eier, milch, und brot?" In a few weeks my conversational German improved considerably. My maternal grandmother had been born in Luxembourg and my grandfather in Belgium. My mother attended a German school in Aurora, Illinois, where her parents were homesteaders, and had grown up speaking and writing the language. She taught me some German as I was growing up.

When he wasn't traveling with the Air Force Team, Bob played #1 singles for the German team at the Wiesbaden Tennis Club. It was an exclusive club, with many wealthy, titled members. They were very serious about tennis and liked to celebrate after winning a match by popping a bottle of champagne. We shared all the amenities, such as the clubhouse and swimming pool, and were guests at their elaborate parties, the only Americans in this group. In July, Bob was invited to play in the Berchtesgaden Invitational of 1953, a prestigious German tournament. He won the singles title, and he and his partner Pierce won the doubles.

By all appearances, Berchtesgaden was a charming mountain town in the Bavarian Alps near the Austrian border. From our hotel window, we could see the Watzmann, the third highest mountain in Germany, and the Konigssee, a glacial lake. However, the beauty we observed was in stark contrast to the tragic history that had taken place nearby. Hitler's headquarters, the Eagle's Nest, was one of the sites where he and his lieutenants created their strategy that resulted in millions of deaths during the war. Although the Eagle's Nest and Hitler's home, Berghoff, were demolished in 1952 by the Bavarian government, their impact remained.

An unexpected event occurred on our way to the Berchtesgaden Invitational when our Fiat, driven by an Air Force staffer, broke down on the autobahn. After our car stalled, we were forced to stand by the side of the road until we were given a ride by a passing motorist who took us to the train station in Salzburg, Austria, where we boarded a train for the twelve-mile trip to Bavaria. After the tournament on our drive back to Wiesbaden, there were some tense moments when our car was stopped at the Austrian checkpoint by a Russian border patrol.

Austria was under joint occupation and Salzburg, the way we had arrived, was in the Western zone. We were now in the Eastern zone. It was late at night and I was tired and unsure of the reason for our interrogation. After showing our passports and giving an explanation as to why we were taking this route (and a gift of a carton of American cigarettes), we were allowed to continue on to Wiesbaden.

During the Octoberfest celebration, we joined other tennis club members in a cavalcade of autos following the lead car up the winding mountain road to a surprise destination. Occasionally, they signaled for everyone to stop beside the highway for a toast with a shot of Schnapps. After our arrival an hour later at the inn on top of the mountain, we were greeted by polka music, dancers in lederhosen, and a dinner of wienerschnitzel, kertalfan, salat, and mugs of lager beer.

In the fall, I was invited to a dinner party at the tennis club when Bob was on the World Tennis Championship tour. Wearing a white party dress with a full crinoline skirt, I met some friends and we sat together at a long table enjoying champagne cocktails. Rather early in the evening, I mentioned to an acquaintance from Denmark that I needed to leave, and he offered to take me home on his motorbike, an interesting prospect in my full skirt and high heels.

That September, we celebrated Bob's win of both the singles and doubles titles with his partner Pierce in the World U.S. Air Force Tennis Championship of 1953, held in Bermuda. To qualify for the world championship, Bob had to win several major tournaments against stiff competition in the European theatre, a feat that he accomplished in part due to his strong service and backhand game. He was one of 32 singles champions representing 16 commands competing for the international honor, which he ultimately captured.

The warm summer days cooled gradually as autumn approached. We celebrated Thanksgiving dinner at the home of Air Force friends. I was remembering the good times we had during our stay, and I thought of the many cities that we visited including Munich, Garmisch, Idar Oberstein, Bad Hamburg, and Salzburg.

My husband's tour of duty in Germany was coming to an end, and we made plans to return to the U.S. I would be flying on the Constellation and Bob would be returning with his Air Force group. He was given an early discharge to attend college in Montana.

A week before our departure, we had a party for some of our young German and American friends. The setting was the Von Jagow's formal dining room, with its ornate table, where their silver and china that been graciously loaned to me for the occasion had been laid out. As I was setting the table, I turned the silver over to read the inscription. There was a swastika on the back of each piece of silver.

I thought about growing up during the war in the 40s and listening to the news on the radio and reading about it in the newspaper. I had four brothers in the military, two of whom were stationed in Europe. My older brother Francis was a sergeant in the U.S. Army Air Force. He was a waist gunner on a B-17 bomber (the Flying Fortress) stationed near London with the RAF and participated in raids over Germany, and was discharged after completing 30 missions. At the same time, my brother Paul had been with the U.S. Army Quartermaster Corps in Paris. We were fortunate that they both came home safely, as we had many friends who had lost family members in the war.

Returning home over New York Harbor, the Statue of Liberty had never seemed so beautiful and welcoming. I looked forward to seeing my family and friends in Indiana.

A box of souvenirs brings back memories. My small, black leather address book, my passport, a train ticket from Salzburg to Berchtesgaden, family photos taken at the Wiesbaden Tennis Club, and a picture of the USAF Tennis Team in uniform on the stairs of a plane, with members holding trophies from the world championship.

On my journey those many years ago, I learned a lot about myself. When I made a promise, I kept it. Although I was young, if I was determined and put my mind to something, I could accomplish it. With the encouragement of my family and the professor, I overcame my fears about traveling to a foreign country, and focused on the experience. Living in a country still dealing with the impact of war made a lasting impression, and made me grateful for what I had. And appreciating what was unfolding in my life in the present moment was a gift I would remember.

MARGUERITE F. McDOLE is a native of South Bend, Indiana, the youngest in a family of 12 children. She raised three daughters, had a career in business, and has enjoyed traveling throughout the U.S. and abroad. Marguerite now lives in McKinney, Texas, where she divides her time between watercolor painting and writing. Several of her memoir essays have appeared in regional publications, including her account of working for Project Skyfire in the pivotal era of the 1950s, which was published in the *Missoulian* and is now part of the archives at the National Museum of Forest Service History.

The Deceptively Slow Motion of Impinging Low Pressure

FRANK LIGHT

Recognized

The monsoon slinks along the ridge
a cat to her prey
syrup off a pancake
old soldiers home on a holiday

FRANK LIGHT has published a number of his poems and essays in various literary journals, many of the latter from a draft memoir entitled *Adjust to Dust: On the Back Roads of Southern Afghanistan.* This short poem first appeared in 2014, under a different title, in O-Dark-Thirty's journal *The Review.*

AGELESS AUTHORS

BONUS SELECTIONS

Nelson Rankin Learns How to Retire

LARRY UPSHAW

Executive Director of Ageless Authors

NELSON RANKIN CRANKED THE VERTICAL BLINDS APART AND watched his wife Joni back her car out of the driveway. He just stood there in his robe and slippers, a man with nowhere to go and plenty of time to get there. He glanced ruefully into his office off the family room. From where he stood, he could see his laptop computer on the desk next to a large monitor he used to look at several emails at a time.

I haven't read emails for days, Nelson thought longingly, *since before the surgery.* They would be filled with all kinds of worthwhile details. But considering the circumstances, there would be hell to pay if Joni caught him with them.

He moved the blinds so he could gaze far down the driveway and know for certain that Joni was gone from the neighborhood. She had to pick up four prescriptions, stop at the grocery store and retrieve their daughter from the elementary school. Nelson had at least two hours before she would return. He walked across the room into the office, turned on the overhead light, sat down at the desk and got busy.

Less than an hour later Nelson, deep in concentration, heard the sliding door scrape open, his wife's voice instructing his daughter. Joni must have gone directly to school and come back instead of running errands. He stood up straight in front of his office chair. Don't look like you're doing anything of note and no one will question you.

"Forgot my debit card," Joni said, peering around the corner with Nelson at the computer. "What's going on here?"

"Just reading some emails," Nelson said. "People wanting to know how I'm doing."

"Can we be sure of that, Mr. Rankin?" Her voice mocked him and he looked quizzically at her. Their daughter peeked around the corner, too, a dour look on her face.

"Daddy, whatcha doing in here?"

"Sweetie, I'm only answering emails. No big deal."

Was he cheating on the two women in his life, being so eager to respond to others?

"Nelson, we know what you're doing," Joni said, "and don't think you'll get away with it. Dr. Hirschfeld won't be happy."

Considering the cloud of gloom the good doctor had attached to Nelson and his illness, his unhappiness was a given.

"Yeah, Daddy," his daughter said. "Didn't the doctor warn you about this?"

"Well, the stress, yeah," he said. "But I'm not stressed, sweet pea. See, I'm not excited. It's just reading."

Joni wasn't buying it. "And where does reading get you, Nelson? Who are you corresponding with?"

"Just clients. They want to know how I'm doing."

"Admit it, Nelson," she said, looking at him straight on. Joni was about to accuse him of the worst. "You're going against your doctor's explicit orders. He told you it was time to slow down. Nelson, is this what it's come to? Do we have to watch you every minute? Monitor who you are with and why? Nelson, were you . . . *working?*"

There he was, busted just a week after a cardiology team took his heart out and played a game of H-O-R-S-E with it. Four cardiac bypasses. A small heart attack on the table. Dire warnings from a doctor who surely saw his life coming to an end.

"You know, Mr. Rankin, you cannot work any longer," Dr. Hirschfeld told him. "The stress will kill you. It's time for you to retire."

And so began the Rankin family's long, strange relationship with work and its polar opposite, retirement. That year his surgery took place, Nelson was just 45 years old, two full decades younger than the normal retirement age. Due to an unfortunate family history and the mysteries of his body, he had been the youngest in coronary ICU, with a mortgage and a young family. How would they live? What would Nelson do with himself?

He was at the apex of his business and professional life. When Nelson was caught sneaking around to take on work projects, his wife didn't simply wag her finger. She feared for his life. Joni worked too. But when Nelson didn't work, they didn't have enough money to pay the bills. It got to the point that the greatest stress factor in his life was NOT working.

Fast forward several years, with Nelson operating at this sub-optimal level into his early fifties. Additional heart problems caused him to get a second opinion on his health. After extensive tests, the new guy thought his original cardiologist was full of it.

"You are not going to die," the new doctor loudly proclaimed. "Work can be rewarding. Not all of it causes stress. If you follow doctor's orders about taking care of yourself, there's no reason you can't live to be as old as all the cranky men patients I deal with every day."

This doctor clearly had a more positive outlook and he gave Nelson a new-found energy and prospective. For the next decade, retirement was the last thing on Nelson's mind. An elderly woman friend in her eighties scolded him like he was a small child if he even mentioned the word.

"Retire and you die," she said. She liked to take the word apart and revise its meaning, like she was dissecting an animal.

"Re-tire, it's like rejuvenate or rebirth," she said. "It's not meant to stop or slow you, but to help you start something new."

Disparaging the concept of retirement meant so much to her that he usually agreed.

"Besides, you don't look old enough to retire," she told him. "Maybe you haven't earned it."

As he edged into his sixties, most people thought Nelson was much younger. As a kid, he was always the baby-faced guy who couldn't buy beer as a teenager. To girls he made a great younger brother. Now as he grew older, his youthful appearance became an asset. Because they had a young daughter, he and Joni palled around with other young parents and Nelson was consumed with work and family, soccer games, graduations and vacations. He looked like the epitome of health.

His only concession to retirement was pumping cash into accounts he could access when the time came. Retirement money is tax deferred. It stays in an account until you are no longer working. By spending it when you are making little or no income, you pay little or no taxes on it. Finally, aging has its merits. Not that Nelson ever thought he would enjoy that benefit personally.

After all, he was living on borrowed time. He figured at some point before he could retire, he would succumb to another heart incident and leave Joni with a tidy sum. Imagine his surprise when he was among the living for his fiftieth high school reunion. He hadn't seen most of these people for half a century, and here he was mingling with a couple hundred of them in a country club ballroom.

"Just think," he whispered to Joni, "all of these people are the same age, 67-68 years old. Some look great after a cushy life, others have been rode hard and put away wet. Is that nature or nurture or both?"

Half a dozen of his old chums on the school newspaper staff gathered at one table and that's where he and Joni spent most of the evening.

"I mostly go to exercise class, and I study mutual funds." A woman who had been an editor explained how she spent her time. "And I still like to write. It's just for fun."

"I haven't written a word since I got out of college," said an overweight man in an expensive suit. On the staff, he had sold advertising, and he worked for three decades as an account executive for a marketing company. "For a long time, I had people to write for me. Of course now, I don't have people." He chuckled at that.

Nelson leaned forward in his chair, listening to the others. Something about their pacing was foreign to him—slower, less aggressive, more relaxed. As a group, they seemed content.

"So how many of you are retired?" he finally asked. They all raised their hands.

"I work part-time," said another woman, "usually 10 to 15 hours a week. I could work more if I wanted, but I don't unless I'm saving for a big trip."

"I went from full-time work to out the door, even had a retirement party," said one man. Others described their retirement as a gradual process, sloughing off hours and responsibilities while collecting a smaller and smaller paycheck. That seemed the reasonable thing to Nelson.

Maybe I have to think about retiring, he thought. How could he be so unprepared? How could this sneak up on him? Did he think he would work forever? Had to admit he was ready to slow down. It was simply a matter of cutting loose clients who were good for his business but really difficult to manage.

In the months after the reunion, he started the process and soon was servicing just a handful of low-stress clients.

At age 70, Nelson signed up for social security benefits. Six months later, he began to take distributions from his retirement accounts as required by tax law. In time, he sent a message to the last of his clients that he was no longer available for paying work.

Nelson Rankin retired once in his forties, but the prospect of it was frightful and he returned to work with a vengeance. Now, after success in the business wars, he has retired for a second time, and this one's for good. The timing is right and he has finally learned how to do it.

Larry Upshaw has enjoyed a 50-year career as a journalist, author, publisher and marketing executive. He began his writing career at the University of Texas at Austin, freelancing for the rotogravure magazine of the *Dallas Times Herald* and staff writer for *Texas Highways*. He wrote for a number of regional and national newspapers and magazines, including *The Dallas Morning News, D Magazine, Atlanta Constitution, Washington Post, Christian Science Monitor, Rocky Mountain Magazine* and the *Denver Post*. As chief executive officer and creative director of Texas Law Marketing, Larry wrote and published a dozen nonfiction books on law, health and business. He co-founded Ageless Authors, where he is now executive director.

A Reading Anthology of Writers Age 65+

Jean W. Yeager

Volunteer Consultant for Ageless Authors

So, WHAT KIND OF READING EVENT WOULD YOU EXPECT IF the writers were all over age 65? It would probably be quite different from the 20-something open mic poetry reading you see at local clubs. That would be fresh, young, maybe raw.

If some of the authors from Ageless Authors were to read from their work, it would be an evening where one story, after a poem, after a memoir, after an essay, would be uniquely different in content and form, but all written to a high level of form and the considerable depth which age and experience gives us.

Michael Coolen would read his first line: "Dad was killed by whales." And the entire room would fall silent. And, Michael's story would carry us into that experience.

Shirley Wright would quietly describe the spooky, eerie moonlit scene and the shadows beneath the scrub oaks in the Texas Hill Country landscape scene as the home invasion perp in her story quietly starts breaking in on the sleeping author/victim inside.

That reading of authors from across the country probably will never happen in one place, space and time being what it is. But, the authors reading at the Phoenix Bookstore in Rutland, Vermont, were just as entertaining and memorable.

A local poet, Bernard Holmes, described himself as a 20-something young man on the streets of New York who took the audience with him into a smoky jazz club and then became the jazz experience with several poems which were written and delivered like jazz riffs (remember jazz), complete with percussive mouth pops and body thumps and vocalized sax-like warbles.

A woman took us into a section of her recent novel, right into the instant where Lauren realizes the reality of her marriage is not a reality at all. It's one of those shivering, falling moments when the earth shifts under your feet. But this isn't the first time Lauren has been on shifting sand and something begins to dawn on her.

Then, a different reality, an in-your-face telling by a man who in 1979 was a safety engineer at Three Mile Island and was on duty at the time when the largest nuclear power plant disaster in U.S. history began. The disaster warning lights began flashing and the sirens blaring, and the "What the hell . . . ?" began to unfold. His chilling memoir kept us riveted to our seats.

You can't tell what you'll experience at an Ageless Authors reading because authors over the age of 65 have done a lot of living and process it in a variety of interesting ways.

The Phoenix Books Ageless Authors event drew a larger than normal reading audience. This is one reason why the Ageless Authors anthology promotional events at the Phoenix Bookstore in Rutland have morphed into a quarterly Ageless Authors reading event.

The first reading included 20+ authors, their friends, family and those from our town. I knew many authors, but there were many I didn't know who were part of more distant writers' groups.

We managed our time by counting noses of who was in attendance and wanted to read and divided the two hours amongst ourselves. A minimum of five minutes helps an author focus what they will read on a particularly strong portion of their work.

This community aspect is really exciting to bookstores. The attendance at readings is dependent upon the pull of the author. And, if the author is not from the local community, that community connection simply can't be present. But, the idea of a reading by authors from your community is appealing.

Will Notte, manager of my local Phoenix Bookstore in Rutland, used the Ageless Authors book jacket as the visual, and me as a local writer as the hook and we invited any or all local authors to come and read from their work, published or not. So, the entire event became much bigger than one guy reading his essay. It became a reading anthology.

I attend several writing groups in my area, and I know writers who attend other writing groups. When I sent them the information about the Phoenix event, it didn't take long to pass an opportunity to come and read your work to a fairly large network of people. Bookstores love this kind of grassroots promotion. And writers tell friends and family and bring them along to the reading, too.

Ageless Authors has launched a unique publishing category with its anthologies of writers age 65+. So, if you've been published in an Ageless Authors anthology, you are a member of a rather unique group which is growing each year. Congratulations!

And, if you're a writer age 65+, and your work is not in an Ageless Authors anthology, you are still in this unique group which is just beginning to be recognized in the publishing world. Each year, the Ageless Authors group conducts a writing contest and the best work is selected for another anthology. So, we've got a bright future—a new publishing category is being born.

It happened before with young adult fiction and nonfiction as a distinct category. Now Ageless Authors is beginning to define a new segment of seasoned writers whose work is qualitatively distinct. What we write about and how we write about it is beginning to be recognized.

My recent peek into publishing trends shows that memoir is the fastest growing segment of adult nonfiction and most of those memoirs are *not* written by the 30- or 40-somethings. Like I say, the Ageless Authors anthologies are catching that memoir wave and staking out the 65+ segment; so approaching your local bookstore helps make this new category they've only read about in trade pubs real. Local bookstores always want to take advantage of any new publishing trend. So, you may be the right person in the right place at the right time.

Ageless Authors hasn't just singled out one writer. We are a collection of writers, a growing community of writers of poetry, fiction, essay, nonfiction, and memoir. And so, it makes sense to add this community approach to your writing/publishing/promotion arsenal.

I've recently tested the concept at a church conference, conducting a reading for authors age 65+ at a large Quaker gathering in a nearby town. With advance notice, and reminders during that conference event, about 15 people read and listened. The bookstore manager was so pleased at the contribution that we have agreed to conduct another at next year's conference.

I've since conducted such readings at several other regional bookstores including Northshire Books in Manchester, Vermont. This is another of the leading chains in our region. And, I will be contacting independent bookstores soon.

If you plan to conduct such an event, you will need to give several months lead time for the bookstore to muster publicity, for you to find local writing groups, and to weave the two together.

Ageless Authors can provide a high-quality image of book covers and other information the bookstore may need for publicity. And, they'll sell you books at a discount so the bookstore can sell them and you both can make some money!

All this confirms that there is a new community of authors defining itself, and that community includes you! Keep writing. Start reading aloud. And contact your local bookstore!

Jean Yeager enjoyed himself so much as a prize winner in the very first Ageless Authors Writing Contest that he decided to lend a hand with development of the group. He worked with Submittable to develop the protocol necessary to submit entries to Ageless Authors contests. Jean has been a professional writer for more than four decades. He started out as a copywriter authoring jingles for 7-11 convenience stores. He is an award-winning essayist, short story writer, playwright and screenwriter. He lives in Rutland, Vermont.

DANG,
I WISH I HADN'T DONE THAT
(REGRETS)

The Klutzwit Gene

a story guaranteed to be 94% accurate

Geoffrey K. Graves

First Prize

MY FATHER WAS NO IDIOT. NINETY-NINE PERCENT OF the time he was level-headed and thoughtful, a good dad and husband, kind-hearted friend to many, an all-around solid human being. Then, there was that other one percent of the time when he did a good impression of a complete fool.

I am of the opinion it was the result of a genetic flaw because the rest of my immediate family, including the one with his fingers on the keys typing these words, had that same issue. There must have been some rogue gene that was comprised of equal parts klutziness and nitwitted-ness. Even my mother had it and she certainly wasn't blood-related to Dad. Maybe it was contagious. Maybe the two together increased the power of it in future generations, a frightening thought. You could call it the klutzwit gene. I will leave it up to others to work that out. If it ever is discovered and the scientific community selects that name, I would like credit as a way to enhance the historical standing of my family. This will exemplify my assertion:

As a youngster, money was always tight in our household. Like many folks who grew up in the Great Depression, rather than hire a professional to paint the modest family home, my parents handled the job themselves. For the indoor painting, Mom used a brush to cut around the doorways, windows, baseboards, ceilings and electric outlets while Dad handled all the rolling. Outside it was basically the same routine except Dad got up on the ladder to handle the cutting above Mom's arm reach because she didn't trust herself climbing ladders. A wise woman.

We often spent weekends down on Balboa Island where we enjoyed budget family entertainment consisting of sunning and swimming in the bay, and the occasional corn dog from the Jolly Roger restaurant outdoor window. It was on Balboa Island my parents spotted a freshly painted home the colors of which appealed to them both, and they decided to paint our house similarly. The background color was ochre and the trim a semi-gloss black. Mom always had a good eye for colors and got our local paint store to precisely match the scheme.

It took my parents a couple weekends to paint the exterior of our little three-bed, two-bath stucco home on McFadden Street in old Santa Ana, California, and they were nearly complete except for one tiny little spot at the peak of the driveway wall. No matter how he stretched from the top rungs of his old wood ladder, my father couldn't quite reach that spot. He came up with the idea to wrap some electrician's tape around a short wood stick affixed to the paintbrush handle extending it far enough to succeed in reaching the final missing bit.

"Got it," he said.

"Good. Now, come on down," Mom directed, she of the opinion the less time spent on a ladder, the better.

Alas, just before starting down Dad accidentally swiped a daub of the ochre-colored paint onto the black trim of the eaves.

"Well, nuts," he said, which was about as salty as he ever got. He looked down at Mom and gave out a big sigh.

"What?" Mom asked.

"Well, lookit," he said.

"What?" she said.

"The trim! Look at the trim!"

"Where?"

"Right there. How can you miss it?" he said, aggravated with himself.

"You mean that blotch?"

"Yes, I mean that blotch."

"That can't stay like that," she said.

"I know that, Maxine. Why do you think I said, 'well, nuts?'"

"You've got to wipe it off."

He re-sighed, then started down the ladder, fetched a rag, soaked a little paint thinner onto it and started back up. But like that last little spot at the peak, there was just no way to reach the blotch on the trim. His ladder was again too short and the location of the ochre blotch on the outer edge of the black eave wouldn't allow him to use the extendo-stick trick for the careful cleaning job required with a thinner-soaked rag. He had to somehow get himself up higher than the ladder allowed to fix his screw-up. Back down the ladder he came.

"I don't know what to do, here," he said, disgusted.

"You can't leave it like that," Mom said. "Everybody will see it and ask, 'What's the deal with the blotch?'"

I was in the house and had my ear cocked to the conversation drifting in through the open kitchen window, and it was at that point my father called me to come out. He pointed up.

"You got any ideas?" he asked.

"Why don't you climb up on the roof and reach over and clean it off?" I proffered.

"Nah. I couldn't see what I was doing and I'd probably mess up more paint than I'd fix," Dad said, shaking his head. "Nuts, nuts, and nuts!"

"I don't see why you don't just go borrow a longer ladder from Ralph or Kenny?" Mom said.

My father instantly said, "No," and both Mom and I knew why. That would be like admitting the neighbor dads had better tools and equipment than Dad had. Men were funny like that in those days—one of the primary measurements of a man's machismo was based upon the contents of his tool shed.

There was a moment of silent pondering, then the klutzwit gene's light bulb went off in Dad's head.

"Tell you what, Geoff, come with me to the garage. I have an idea."

We walked back to the garage where he had me grab one of his two six-foot tall wood stepladders and he took the other. We carried them back over to the wall where my mother stood with her arms crossed and the blotch above awaited correction.

My mother said, "What in the world are you doing?"

"Just relax. You'll see."

"If you're thinking what I think you're thinking," she said, "you've got to be kidding."

"What?" my dad said with a little trill to the word.

"What are you going to do with those?" she asked.

"Just never you mind. Stay here. We'll be right back," he said. "Geoff..." And he indicated I should again follow him, this time to the little narrow alleyway behind the garage where he kept an old woodpile. There, he lifted one end of a heavy, long two-by-twelve plank left over from an abandoned picnic table project of his. We wiped the spiders and their white puffball eggs off it and together carried it back to the site of the blotch.

Mom: "You are thinking what I thought you were thinking. Have you lost your mind?"

Dad: "Just help me with this, would you? Please?"

Over the next few minutes we built a thing that looked like some contraption out of an old Hal Roach Laurel and Hardy movie. It started with the two six-foot-tall stepladders set about 12 feet apart, the tops perpendicular to the wall. The plank was placed across the top from one to the other, then somehow my father muscled that heavy old wood extension ladder up onto the plank, leaning its top against the house and the feet of the ladder centered on the plank. My mother and I were sternly instructed to each hold one of the stepladders while my father steadied the extension ladder nailing the feet of it to the plank and nailing the plank to the top of our stepladders.

"I'm not going to do this," Mother flatly stated.

"Maxine, if you and Geoff will just hold the ladders steady, I'll be up and down before you know it," he said with a tone of voice indicating come hell or high water, he was going up there to get that doggone blotch and we were to do whatever he told us to do to help him make that happen.

"I'm going to close my eyes. I can't watch this," Mom said.

"Just hold the ladder firmly, pretty please, dear. You don't have to keep your eyes open if you don't want to."

And up he started. He took it slowly, gingerly, step-by-step. Mom and I found we had to put a little shoulder work into keeping each of our ladders upright and steady but believe it or not, he made it up far enough to reach the blotch. He was hanging onto the extension ladder with his left hand, getting ready to wipe the blotch with the rag in his right. The height of his head was just below the peak, about 20 feet above the concrete driveway surface.

"He made it up, Mom," I announced since she wasn't looking.

"Fine. Just tell me when he's down."

"Oh, no," Dad said.

And, plop. Just when things were going so well, Dad dropped the rag.

"He dropped the rag, Mom."

Mom opened one eye and looked down at the rag, then peered up at Dad.

"Now what?" she asked, her words dripping with displeasure.

"One of you's going to have to reach over there and get the rag and toss it up to me."

"For crying out loud, Glenn, I can't reach that rag while still holding onto this ladder."

I stretched one hand out as far as I could and still steady my ladder with the other, but it was a no-go for me, too.

"Me neither, Dad."

Looking down, Dad sucked on his teeth a minute, a habit indicating he was thinking things over.

"Geoff, you're closer to it. Just let go and grab the rag quickly, then get back to the ladder and toss the rag up to me."

"Good gravy," Mom moaned.

"Hey! What's going on over there?" neighbor Ralph Shelton poked his head out the bathroom window of his home that looked onto our driveway. He had a big grin on his face.

"Hi, Ralph," Mom said. "Glenn's decided to end his life in grand fashion. We're helping him do it."

"Do you need a hand?" Ralph asked. "I mean helping him with, well, whatever it is he's doing? I don't mean, uh, killing him."

"Nope, but thanks, Ralph," Dad intoned loud and clear in case any other neighbors were within earshot. "We've got it all handled," he said.

"Okay," Ralph said, unsurely. "Be real careful up there."

"Thanks, again, Ralph."

Dad waited for Ralph to close the window, but Ralph wasn't going to close the window. This show was too good to pass up.

"Now get the rag, Geoff."

"I don't know, Dad, I just don't think it's going to. . . ."

"Get the darn rag and toss it up here! . . . Please."

I let out a really big gush of air, and said, "Okay."

And that was it. The second I let go of my ladder the laws of physics entered the ring with the klutzwit gene and the gene predictably lost. The whole thing came crashing down into a tangled heap of ladders, plank and Dad. Mom and I both jumped back to avoid being crushed by the calamity. The plank alone probably weighed 50 pounds. The noise was incredible, and above it all were quadruple screams, one from each of my parents, one from me and one from Ralph. Mom and I ran over to see how Dad was.

"Are you okay?" Mom's voice wavered.

We pulled the ladders away from Dad who sat there in shock for a few minutes catching his breath. We started taking an inventory of his body. He felt around here and there, and eventually pulled himself up to his feet. Miraculously, nothing seemed to have broken, cracked or split open. Luckily, his glasses wound up in a bush against the opposite wall. I heard Ralph slowly close his window, then I heard some muffled laughter and these words directed to his wife: "Oh, my gosh, Almarie, you are not going to believe what that Glenn Graves has done, now."

"Sure you're okay," Mom asked?

"Yeah, I think so. My wrist is a little sore," he said, at which we all looked at his right wrist and saw a golf-ball sized lump had sprouted out of it.

"Uh-oh," Dad said. "Actually, that hurts a lot."

"That might be broken," Mom mumbled flatly. "Why don't you just sit over there on the front porch for a minute and take a breather," she said. "Geoff, help me clear this mess up so we can get the car out and take your father to Dr. Davidson's."

There was quite a little group in the waiting room to see the doctor who had delivered both my sister and me some years before. That room always had an unpleasant antiseptic odor wafting through the air. We sat biding time in those chairs made of chrome and black plastic leatherette till eventually they called Dad's name and in he went. He later related to us the conversation he had with our good family physician, Dr. L.C. Davidson.

At the time of the ladder collapse catastrophe, Dr. Davidson was probably pushing 60 so his wavy gray hair had already thinned out. Black horn-rimmed glasses were perched atop his little bulb of a Santa Claus nose. He wore one of those white short-sleeved doctor shirts made of a slightly translucent fabric that for whatever reason matched his nurses' uniforms: 1960s medical fashion. Dr. Davidson always spoke with a calm soothing nasally voice that made you feel like nothing would ever rile him up.

Dr. Davidson: "Hello, Mr. Graves. How have you been?"

Dad: "Just fine, Doc, thanks. You know, other than. . . ."

Dr. Davidson: "Good. Good. Nurse took your vitals. Everything looks A-OK, there."

Davidson looked down at Dad's wrist and said, "Say, how long have you had that lump on your wrist?"

Dad: "Doc, that's why I'm here."

Davidson: "Good. Good. What happened?"

Dad: "I fell off a ladder. Well, some ladders."

Davidson: "Ladders! Did you? Good. Good. Sounds like an interesting story, there. Well, happens all the time. You'd be surprised."

Dad: "It was my first time."

Davidson: "I see. Let's make it your last, hm? Heh-heh."

Dad: "Yeah, I think I learned my lesson."

Davidson: "Smart man. Good. Good. Glenn, I want to take a gander at that wrist over here where the light's a little better. Bring it on over and lay it on my desk. Yeah, right there. That's good. Good."

Davidson gently prodded the lump.

"Um hm. That feel a little tender, there, does it?"

"That it does," Dad winced at the prodding.

Then Dr. Davidson picked up a big book.

Davidson: "Say, I've been reading this novel by Katherine Anne Porter, *Ship of Fools.* You heard of it?"

"No. Can't say I have."

"Got it through the Book-of-the-Month Club. It was on the *New York Times* Best Sellers List for six months. Imagine that! Must be some kind of record, don't you think?"

Dad: "I really wouldn't know, Doc, I haven't. . . ."

And with that, Dr. Davidson slammed the thick book down hard on Dad's lump.

Out in the lobby and for the second time that day my mother and I heard a blood-curdling scream that sounded an awful lot like the first blood-curdling scream we had heard earlier while Dad descended hands-free from the ladder. Mom grabbed my hand, all the babies started crying, a Mexican lady with three kids shouted out "Dios Mio!" and everyone in the waiting room went saucer-eyed including the nurse at the reception desk who shot up and out of her chair and said, "I'm sure everything is fine, everybody. I'll just check to see if the Doctor killed anything I mean needs anything. Needs!" and she rushed through the door into the back offices.

Minutes later she came out with my father, who appeared to be shell-shocked. With her arm around him, she guided him wobbling shakily over to us where he sagged down into one of the chrome/leatherette chairs. He'd really had quite a day and looked it.

"What happened in there," Mom asked softly?

"He hit my lump with a *Ship of Fools*."

"What!?"

"Yeah. It's a fat book."

"What!?"

"Six months on the *Times* bestseller list."

"What kind of medicine is that?"

"He said that's what you do with that kind of lump. He even showed me in a medical journal where it said that's what's called for. I wish he'd given me a little bit of a heads up before he whacked it, but he said it's better if you don't know what's coming, and I guess I kind of agree with him," Dad said.

"I don't know that I agree with him. He could have given you a heart attack," Mom said.

"Anyway, the lump's gone, now," Dad smiled weakly.

And it was. There was just a red mark that Davidson said would eventually go away. Dad wound up borrowing a ladder from Kenny

Turtenwald who lived on the other side of our house from Ralph Shelton, and believe it or not that same day he went back up and got that antagonistic blotch. The house looked pretty darn good with its new paint job, and my parents got a lot of compliments on it.

If there is a moral to this story, it's this: You can learn things from your parents they didn't intentionally teach you. Many years after, I found myself up on a lightweight Home Depot aluminum ladder and that whole experience came back to me just as I reached up to paint that last little bit on the high peak of the roof of my own home. I got the job done without incident, but I'd never have a story like that to tell my son. Of course, if you asked him, he'd probably tell you there were plenty of others to make up for it. That klutzwit gene still runs strong in our DNA.

Geoffrey K. Graves was formerly creative director and owner of Graves Advertising, winner of many awards. He taught Interpersonal Communication at Rancho Santiago College District. He co-authored (with Jonas Flagg) *Seven Days to Disaster* (Major Books), and wrote *Bakers Dozen,* a screenplay optioned by Columbia Pictures and a semi-finalist in the 2017 Chicago Table Read My Screenplay competition. He also worked in the Script Department at CBS Television City, Hollywood. He's recently completed a collection of humorous short stories entitled *Way Out On A Limb.*

In the Midst of Life

MARC HESS

Second Prize

THIS WHOLE GRAVESIDE THING JUST CHAFES ME. HAD I the better fortune to be born in the next generation we'd be done with this barbaric ritual and these acres of idle tombs could be used to house the living; condominiums and high-rises for the homeless. Ha! Raul would have loved that. Had we stayed friends, I could have brought this idea to him, he could have made a campaign out of it, and—in his inevitable political style—gone on and screwed it all up. Instead we're now going to stick him under one of these archaic markers, making what's left of him part of the problem.

What am I doing here with these long-faced pretenders unfolding themselves from parked cars, popping up their black umbrellas and tromping off across this soggy headstone patch just so they can be done with their colleague? I, too, have to walk across this wet lawn, ruining forever my only pair of black peep-toe pumps. And, to be honest, I never liked that man.

"You okay?" Thomas leans in to ask. The perfect husband, he holds our umbrella at an awkward angle to keep the light mist off of me.

There is a sincerity in his eyes that I don't deserve so I force a weak smile to reassure him. It's not what he thinks. But that's my fault. I let him invent his version of this story—encouraged it actually—that Raul and I had been college lovers. Maybe Thomas imagined that Raul was my first fuck and that it had ended badly, which provides a perfectly believable explanation for 40-some years of overt bitterness toward this dead guy, along with some perverse fascination that has always had a hold on me. Yes, I had been a close follower of Raul's raucous political career but I never, not once, voted for him. I nagged Thomas to never vote for him either. Once, over Sunday morning coffee and newspapers, I went off on a rant about Raul's antics on the city council as Thomas just peered over the top of his sports pages and said sheepishly, "Baby, I, too, had some flings that I would prefer to forget and I am so happy that I ended up with you." Always protecting me. Always letting me off the hook. I let him go with that because the truth is so much more unforgivable. Even now, as we squish our way toward the huddle of raincoats and umbrellas punctuating this mushy cemetery, that recollection has my stomach churning, feeling like the lie that could rear up at any moment and be the absolute end of me.

A dark green canvas awning covers only a small part of the gathering and bears the name of the funeral home along with that peculiar silhouette of a Victorian horse-drawn hearse. Protected somewhat from the drizzle, a somber crowd is packed under it shoulder to shoulder, but still willing to shuffle over to make room for another. Thomas, his firm hand under my elbow, guides me under the cover more forcefully than I would have liked. I hadn't intended to be so front-and-center. Good grief, these people are so sad. Choked sniffles and tears burst out here and there like an aging water heater trying to tell you it's about to blow. Between slouched shoulders, I can now see the coffin on its gurney and the hole in the ground—steep and neatly dug with a carpet on each side. That sends a chill down my spine. A phalanx of granite-faced men in dark coats and neckties stand behind a row of chairs, each with their hands clasped over their groins, suitably somber—the suits from city hall now making a show of mourning the very man they had spent their careers trying to bury. They could never out-politic the old maverick. No one had the balls to assassinate him, they just had to wait for him to die. Standing with them, their obligatory wives each wearing outfits perfect for the occasion. I rise up, just a bit, on my damp toes and cock my head, but I can't see what they do for footwear when the occasion calls for heels on damp lawns.

"O God whose mercies cannot be numbered..."

The priest's opening words draw the attention to the bier which allows me the opportunity to sneak a look around. I am surprised, even impressed, at the number of people, most of them outside the awning in the rain: tradesmen, spiffy young socialites, moms with their kids, leather-vested bikers and gangster-types, and old geezers from Raul's university days—of which I am one. Raul would have been proud of the coalition he has finally pulled together. I have a fair view of a rough fellow in leather and chains, tattoos crawling up his neck, who is crying uncontrollably—probably a bit out of character for him. I strain to make out a red patch in the folds of his jacket that may bear the red-fisted symbol of the old SDS. Such things have become meaningless kitsch over time but, who knows, this guy may be one of those fervent followers that Raul had so often let down. Perhaps this one still believes.

"Accept our prayers on behalf of our servant
William Richard Matthew Alpert, and grant him..."

All eyes rise when the priest speaks the name as it is written on the deceased's baptismal certificate. Everyone here had only known him as Raul; Raul Alpert; or in the headline that he preferred: *Raul the Firebrand*. The trio directly in front of me—a woman flanked by two men in high-collared coats—trade inquisitive whispers with each other. I am one of the very few who had known him before he renamed himself Raul.

"Gives me more revolutionary cred," he had told me way back then.

"And who's going to follow a guy named Dick to the barricades?" I had sassed back. A rising chuckle overcomes me at that recollection. At a funeral? How inappropriate, and now welling up into a full giggle. Choking the laugh releases something of a snort. My hands rush to cover my face and fend off the condescending, over-the-shoulder glance from the lady in front of me. Thomas' arm around my shoulder helps with my cover. I take a deep breath and give another peek at the old SDSer who is still over there crying away, poor soul. He is really hurting and I am over here trying to suppress my laugh.

"Into thy hand, O merciful savior, we commend thy servant, William, a sheep of thine own fold, a lamb of thine own flock, a sinner of thine own redeeming."

Had he not been nailed down inside that coffin, the Raul that I knew would have leapt up and torn those words apart. He so enjoyed disrupting things: heckling speeches, shouting down opponents and drawing attention to himself. The church funeral had to have been at the insistence of his older sister, Charlotte, whom I had never formally met. That must be her over there in the row of chairs, chin-high to the coffin. A lady of more traditional values, from head to toe in proper black, she dabs at the mascara beneath her veil with a tissue. Raul had told me that she vehemently objected to his lifestyle and politics, but the only public statement I heard from her was, "He is my brother and I love him." I like her for that. With her in the seated section are Raul's two younger sisters—I had met one of them but I can't remember which. The rest of the chairs are taken up by three of Raul's wives. That must be embarrassing for them. The youngest of them, with the dark hair and the squirmy children must be the current Mrs. Maria Alpert, the official widow.

"Thomas," I whisper, "Are ex-wives widows, too?"

Glancing about as if I'm disrupting the funeral he whispers back, "I'm not really sure."

The lady in front of me rolls her head back with her answer. "Certainly not if they remarry."

Even in mourning, the widow is pretty. I imagine that she loves Raul and is proud to have his children. For Raul, I had discerned, it was a marriage of political convenience. They hooked up right after Raul had taken a well-earned drubbing at the polls. In his subsequent absence the council passed a resolution aimed directly at him mandating that all future candidates for city office must be ad valorem tax paying residents of the precinct that they represent. So Raul purchased a bungalow in the barrio of one of his fringe constituencies, married Maria, the daughter of a local car dealer, somehow repositioned himself as a champion of Latino rights, and came roaring back into office with a landslide victory.

> *"Dust thou art, and unto dust shall thou return. All we go down to the dust; yet even at the grave we make our song: Alleluia, alleluia, alleluia."*

Thomas keeps an expressionless face through this ordeal and I am trying my best to mimic him. My feet are wet. I am getting tired of standing so I take his arm. He smiles down on me for the briefest of moments then returns to his stoic pose. Thomas would have stood on the opposite end of the political spectrum. He didn't care for Raul's kind at all. Once he said to me, "I'm glad that you grew out of your radical *daze*." Yes, he had used the word *daze* like it had been some kind of stoner phase of my life. Thomas had meant to be cute, and I wanted him to love me, but I still can't shake off the feeling of resentment. Oh, Thomas loves my pluck, and the way I raise his children, and charm his family, and how my liberal attitude plays out in bed. But he doesn't take me seriously.

For my part I didn't like Raul even back in that "radical *daze*," rather we shared a cause. At least back then I believed in something. Sure, something that went so terribly wrong, something—as Thomas said—that I grew out of. But, damn it, it was important to me, and I cared. That was the last time I felt I was really alive—doing something that mattered. And Raul took me seriously. Very seriously.

> *"Into paradise may the angels lead thee, and*
> *at thy coming may the martyrs receive thee..."*

My God, is this priest never to stop? He's dead, already, let it be over.

The one and only time I went out with Raul I was a 21-year-old humanities student. I wore a skirt and make-up so it would look as if we were on a date. We came up from the shadows behind the townhouse with two gasoline bottles stuffed inside my hippie shoulder bag. We both wore gloves. When Raul cocked the first one over his shoulder and I put a match to the rags, his wild hair and unshaven cheeks were illumined in a flickering halo of yellow and bright orange—as if I had brought a gilded saint to life. Raul galloped out of the shadows and up the sidewalk, pulling the flare over his head. I watched as the torch whirled in a semi-circle the length of his arm, crossed over the top of the wrought-iron fence and splattered against a trash can. A stream of blue flames oozed harmlessly along a back alley wall. Even, now, standing at his graveside, I can feel the cold silence of that moment, the nauseous odor of spilt gasoline and the adrenaline that surged through the two of us. Saints no more, in that moment we became mere street vandals.

"The other one!" Raul returned, panting hard. "Light the other one." We fumbled. Our hands shook. Somewhere a dog barked and we both froze and stared into each other's wide eyes—my most intimate moment with him. Finally, after a long and frightening nano-second Raul was off again with a flame held high over his head. This time he crossed the sidewalk in long, athletic strides like a footballer. From a wild round-house pitch the second fireball arched through the air followed by a crash of plate glass and a bright orange glow that crept up the inside curtains as if in a celebration. Raul sashayed back to me, grinning ear-to-ear, silhouetted by the flaming window. He put my hand on his arm and we just strolled away as if nothing was amiss.

At the exact same moment we torched the townhouse three other members of our cadre ignited a pipe bomb at the garage door of a little-known police office just two blocks away. One garage door, one trash can and some burnt-up window curtains—our blow for the oppressed of the world.

"Blessed are the dead who die in the Lord:
Even so saith the Spirit, for they rest from their labors."

I remember the evil feeling that came over me soon after the action when the first of our cadre died. A car ran over his bicycle killing him instantly. The first thought that ran through my head was *he won't be telling anyone.*

It got scarier for me as we all went our separate ways. Who knew what changes we'd go through: who might want to brag about it or need to purge their guilty conscience? For my part, I just disappeared inside a meaningless life; got married and had my children—as if all that would wash me clean.

At my twentieth class reunion—all of us successfully mediocre and responsible parents by now—I heard that another of the cadre had died in a freak industrial accident someplace up north. I inquired no further, but I mentally checked him off my list.

Some years after that I heard that Sally, our "Sally the Red," had cancer. Like Raul and me, she had stayed in the city. Unlike me, she stayed involved as a community organizer. It took a great deal to gather the nerve to visit her and I'm happy that I did. We didn't speak of the action and I didn't even know that she died until Thomas read me her obituary. That just left Raul and me.

Until last Tuesday that is, when he made his final speech and certainly his most memorable. Forty-seven years after our "date," Raul keeled over with a massive coronary in a city council meeting while railing against one of his colleagues as the chairman ferociously hammered his gavel calling "Out of Order! Out of Order!" All of it captured on the CCTV.

So I totally got away with it. The mantle of secrecy falls to me and me alone. I am lighter now, less in need of my husband's shoulder.

"In the midst of life we are in death."

The ladyship before me is attempting to share some observation with her two escorts, craning her neck then whispering alternatively to one then the other. The high collared men tip their ears to her in turns, each one picking up every other a piece of her story . . . so many girl friends . . ." I catch random bits from each side of the conversation, ". . . wasn't more of a scandal . . ." before she cranes her head further back to catch me eavesdropping.

I smile to her and say, in a full normal voice, "I never had sex with him."

She quickly turns away as the two men on either side of her, in one choreographed motion, turn their wanton eyes around to me. As does the couple to my left. And Thomas.

Matter-of-factly I add, "We set a building on fire."

I watch their mouths drop. Thomas shifts his body toward me and says in a scolding whisper. "Karen!"

"It was the Chancery House. We torched it. Raul and I." I nod to assure him that he has heard correctly. "Back in our radical *daze*."

As if on cue, everyone snaps back into their face-forward funeral poses.

The priest drones on. The widows continue to weep. That old SDSer is wiping his eyes. I bow my head in an effort to stifle my rude chortle. My good shoes are ruined and the big toe on my left foot is beginning to poke through a small tear in my stocking. I press my toes to help it push through—this, too, is amusing to me. Then slowly, almost mischievously, I use my right foot to free my entire left foot from that ruined black peep-toe pump. I quietly remove the other one, kick it aside and stand flat on the damp grass, wiggling my toes in the slosh. I am so much more comfortable now.

Marc Hess is a professional editor of travel and regional magazine/websites, and serves on the Board of the Writers League of Texas. Recent nonfiction articles of his have been published in *Sierra* magazine, *Sail* magazine, *Ten West Living* and the *San Antonio Express News.* He can be reached at mhess@hctc.coop or www.marc-hess.com.

Morning Thunder

Richard Perreault

Third Prize

HADE PICKETT WASN'T THE ONLY MAN IN FRUITION, North Carolina to wake up with a woman in bed beside him that Sunday morning, but he was likely the only one trying to figure out what to do with the body.

The woman was face down under the covers, sprawled diagonally across the gnarled oak bed Hade had gotten at the Sisters of Mercy Thrift Shop shortly after he'd moved into the cabin on Stink Dog Creek. The bottom third of her tree-trunk legs jutted from beneath the shroud-like sheet, her feet, luminescent in the gray light of dawn through the never-washed windows.

When Hade awoke, he had been uncertain if he wanted to rouse the hulking figure beside him. He lay quietly waiting for the flotsam in his brain to settle, to expose at least a jagged tip of an explanation of who the woman was and how she came to be in his bed. When none of the mosaic pieced together, he'd cautiously nudged her shoulder with the palm of his hand.

No response.

Harder.

Nothing.

Hade reached beneath the covers intending to give the shoulder a vigorous shake but recoiled when he felt the icy skin beneath his fingers.

Struggling to right himself, he located the mangled paper clip he kept by the bed to secure the nubs of charred, smoked-down joints as he sucked out the last of their nurturing marrow. Steadying his aim, he jabbed the tip of the unwound metal into the woman's arm.

Still no response.

He lay there a moment longer, awash in the acrid smell of sweat, the stale aroma of last night's alcohol, and a pungent musk that might have been the reminiscence of near-unconscious sex or perhaps the early hours of decomposition. When he freed his feet from the sheets and swung them to the floor, they clinked against two empty bottles he recognized as having once been liters of Jose Cuervo Gold. In the hierarchy of debilitating alcohols, for Hade, tequila was at the top. He'd been told he once danced naked atop a bar in Ciudad Juarez after a night of three-for-one margaritas. He had no reason to doubt the story.

Hade assumed he'd done his part to empty the bottles lying at his feet, and figured it was the woman doing her part that had done her in. Maybe the tequila along with something else she'd ingested. He'd seen stories on television about how the combination of too much alcohol and any variety of other things could send someone to the Great Happy Hour in the Sky.

Not bothering to pull so much as a T-shirt onto his naked body, Hade shuffled into the kitchen and began fumbling with the coffee maker. He needed caffeine. He needed to think.

With polluted blood thundering through his head, he struggled to reassemble the shards of the previous night. He'd made his usual Saturday appearance at the Down and Dirty just after nine. Jake, behind the bar, pulled a pitcher of Miller without being asked. By midnight Hade was using his third pitcher of beer to wash down tequila, a holy water notorious for inspiring religious experiences. Even beyond the reputed bar-top dance in Mexico, the golden elixir had more than once conjured hallucinations in Hade's wobbling brain and left him on his knees, worshipping at a porcelain altar, praying for death, calling out the Lord's name, albeit in vain.

Hade started as a clap of thunder shook the cabin, rolling through the valley as though God were telling jokes and the Devil laughing. Hade hadn't heard the punch line, but he was fairly sure the joke was on him.

Hade didn't know who the woman was, which meant she probably wasn't from Fruition. That was good. Nobody local would miss her and that would buy him a little time. But a little time to do what?

Bracing himself with the edge of the counter, he bent down and looked out the narrow window above the sink. A gathering of sodden clouds roiled across the distant peaks off toward Burnsville. A boney, golden finger of celestial fire jabbed at the mist-shrouded forest. Again, the thunder pealed and echoed across the valley. Morning thunder wasn't common in the mountains, but so far nothing about this particular morning had been common.

At the head of the driveway the front end of Hades gray and primer-red pickup was nosed into a large hickory, evidence of one of the many misjudgments he had apparently made the night before. There was no other vehicle, which probably meant the woman had ridden from the bar with him. If she'd left her car at the Down and Dirty, as soon as people started heading that way after church somebody would notice. Someone would remember her and who she'd left with.

Hade ran an imprecise measure of water into the carafe then sloshed the contents into the battered Mr. Coffee 10-Cup Thermal Programmable Coffee Maker that had stopped being programmable long before it arrived at Sisters of Mercy, where it was thrown in for free as an incentive for Hade to buy the oak bed.

Beside the coffee maker sat a purse, a tufted pouch of wool and wood reminiscent of the macramé bags his mother made before Hade was born; in what she referred to as the days before her sweet bird of youth up and flew away.

Hade glanced over his shoulder to make sure he wasn't being watched, though who might be watching him he couldn't have said. He pulled a faded leather wallet from the purse, flipped it open, and held it up to the light. The glowering face of Matilda Deborrah Scruggs stared back at him from the lower left-hand corner of a North Carolina driver's license.

Her weight showed as 220 pounds, but Hade figured she probably was closer to his 250. Everybody lied about their weight on their license, didn't they? According to the license she was 37, three years Hade's senior, and lived in Black Mountain. That was down east of Asheville, a hell of long drive from Fruition over narrow mountain roads. Hade doubted she'd come all the way from Black Mountain just to have a drink at the Down and Dirty. But where Matilda Scruggs had come from wasn't his main concern. What Hade needed to figure out was where she was going next.

If Matilda didn't weigh more than the 220 pounds her license claimed, Hade thought he might be able to get her out of the bed and move her wherever he needed. It would be a struggle, but he didn't see an alternative. He sure as hell wasn't going back to bed that night with her still in it.

Outside, another round of thunder row-row-rowed itself down the valley, sending a murder of crows into a momentary cawing frenzy. A pale mist spritzed the hillside above the cabin, but the heavy rain, for the moment at least, was keeping its distance.

Wet weather would make the rocks above the waterfall at Stink Dog Waller more slippery than usual. If he could lug the body to the top of the falls and toss it off, he might create a believable scenario that she had slipped and fallen from the escarpment. That's what happened to Elisha Mitchell, the man who'd proved the mountain that now bore his name was the highest peak east of the Mississippi. Nobody had ever questioned the veracity of that story, so it was at least plausible.

What Matilda was doing up at the falls on a rainy Sunday morning would be for the authorities to figure out. Of course, figuring out things like that was exactly what the authorities were authorities at doing. They'd know right away the cause of death wasn't a fall. Even if she landed in the creek, soon enough they'd be able to rule out drowning. Then the real questions would begin. Maybe it would be best to get rid of the body all together.

Through the window Hade studied a copse of sumac shrubs shrouded in fog, the leaves still bleeding October blood. Beside the bushes sat the wood chipper he'd borrowed from his nearest neighbor a mile down the road. He'd thought he might someday, before winter, clear the brushy clutter relentlessly encroaching on the cabin.

He recalled a movie and a couple of television shows where a wood chipper had been put to macabre, but effective, use in disposing of bodies. He'd probably have to cut Matilda up to get her into the chipper, but he wasn't yet sure he wouldn't have to cut her up just to get her out of the house.

A chainsaw would be easiest, but a handsaw would cause less spatter. Either way, cutting up a body was bound to create a mess. The wood chipper might render the pieces unrecognizable to the untrained eye, but the splattered gore would go everywhere. He'd seen enough detective shows to know the tiniest incriminating particle of Matilda Scruggs could hang around forever and eventually be found and identified by forensic experts. He could see the scene play out in the segment after the final commercial: The cops, satisfied Hade had nothing to do with the woman's disappearance, would be about to leave when one of them would notice a glob of sanguine matting in Hade's eyebrow, then a fleck of something fleshy on the collar of his flannel shirt.

Realizing he was naked, Hade pulled his tattered, thigh-length down jacket out of the closet by the front door and bundled himself against the chill; a chill that seemed to have started inside of him and was now working its way outward. He knelt beside the hearth, but thought better of kindling a flame. If it came to it, he could cut Matilda into pieces and burn her a chunk at a time, or even stuff her body up the chimney. He studied the damper opening and considered the girth of the woman in his bed. He'd have to remove the flue—no small task—then when he was done with Matilda, seal the chimney to keep the stench from permeating the cabin. He'd smelled skunks passing by on the outside, so he doubted a little brick and mortar would block the odor of a decaying body. Besides, he'd need to buy the mortar. The police could trace the receipt like they unfailingly did when domestic terrorists bought fertilizer for homemade bombs. They'd eventually figure out what he'd done. He'd have accomplished nothing beyond screwing up his fireplace. Whatever the solution, it couldn't include buying anything.

Hade rose from the hearth, snugged the jacket around him, and headed back to the bedroom. Maybe looking at the body, sizing it up, would help him visualize a workable plan. Besides, before deciding what to do, he needed to know if he could lift Matilda Scruggs out of the bed.

The floor creaked beneath his feet. In the distance the storm groaned and growled conspiratorially. The mist had turned to rain, pelting the windows, priming the leak at the corner of the bathroom door.

Hade stepped into the bedroom and flipped the light switch, splashing the hulking figure on the bed in a garish yellow-white glow. He studied the sheet-cloaked lump, a hibernating bear beneath a blanket of snow. "Two twenty ain't even close," he muttered.

A plan began to develop. If he kept Matilda's body wrapped in the sheet, he could use it for leverage and more easily drag her to wherever it was he decided she needed to be. Wrapped up, the body was also less likely to leave telltale traces of DNA or other clues for the investigators to find with their magic dust that turned invisible things a spooky blue when scanned by an equally magical light.

Battling a hint of nausea, Hade knelt on the edge of the bed and unsuccessfully tried to tuck the sheet under the beached-whale frame of Matilda Scruggs. He lifted, poked and prodded, but managed to wedge no more than a few inches of the sheet beneath the body.

Swinging onto the bed like he was mounting a horse, Hade straddled Matilda and forced his hands beneath her shoulders. With a grunt, he lifted her upper torso but lost his grip when he reached with one hand to slip the sheet underneath. He positioned himself for better leverage, again working his hands beneath the body. He was working up a second grunt and lift when a muffled sound from the bedclothes stopped him cold.

"Not now, Hun," the lump beneath him murmured into the pillow. "I got to have my coffee first. Then more rumpity-bumpity. I promise."

Hade didn't move, didn't speak, and until he thought to do so, didn't breathe.

A large, meaty hand swung up from beneath the sheet and firmly grasped his rear end. "You got coffee in this dump, don't you?"

Hade freed himself from Matilda's grip and stumbled toward the kitchen, neither bothering nor daring to look back.

He lifted a dirty mug out of the sink and filled it with coffee. He'd only made enough for one cup but thought it best he give it all to the woman calling to him from the bedroom.

"Rustle us up some breakfast while you're in there," her voice rumbled down the hallway.

Hade didn't bother with cream or sugar. Matilda sounded like the kind of woman who'd take her coffee black and probably her toast too.

"Bacon, eggs, grits, and biscuits would be good," Matilda called out. "Cheese grits if you can do it, and if you're not all that great with biscuits, you can smother them in gravy. Enough gravy'll cure anything."

Hade hesitated, looking out the window across the mountains where it appeared the storm had reconsidered its plans for the day and was heading back toward the cabin.

"And ham and sausage if you got them," the voice from the bedroom continued. "A pancake or two. I guess waffles would be too much to ask. If you don't have real maple syrup, Aunt Jemima's okay, as long as it's not that sugar-free shit. I'll go to the store later and get us something for dinner."

Hade could feel the vibration of a thunderclap as the storm worked its way back across the valley. He closed his eyes and leaned against the sink. It looked like getting rid of Matilda Scruggs was going to be even harder than he had originally thought.

Richard Perreault lives on a mountaintop in western North Carolina overlooking the Great Smoky Mountains National Park. Up there in the rare air, he says, he receives massive amounts of support, inspiration, and tolerance from his wife, Sue, and their cairn terrier, Darci Gayle.

That Ol' Certainty

JOHN HUNTER

Honorable Mention

I SWEAR TO GOD I DID NOT GO TO THE BROKEN SPOKE, that honky-tonk in Austin, looking for that old certainty. Honestly, I just like country music... oh, yeah, and the women. (They can even be asymmetrical! I've got no adipose tissue issue.)

And, I do like the beer, cold Lone Star beer, 'n' I just like to dance the Two-Step. That's all.

Just exercising my emotions; okay, my passions and I'll ask a pretty woman, or two, to dance. Hold her real close, left hand in her right hand, slightly cupped; my right hand on her lower back, maybe her back belt-loop. Catch a beat or two... and we Texas Two-Step. Slow-Quick-Quick; Slow-Quick-Quick; rinse with a cold Lone Star, repeat.

It's just a certainty, that's all. That ol' certainty.

Some gals don't like to be held tight and kinda try to wiggle away. Some don't like to be led and resist for a moment. Then I ask them, "Do you REALLY want to dance?" Some want to be independent, but the Two-Step, well when you Two-Step and you twirl, go open-style and cut your way through the traffic, somebody BETTER lead so it will be less loco and more motion in the locomotion.

So there I was Two-Steppin' and Swing Dancin' and the band was stylin' George Jones 'n' Ray Price 'n' and Willie 'n' Merle and George Strait, Clint, Hank Jr. and, Lord knows who else!

There are layers and layers of lights and boots and hats and glitter and see-through blouses, 'n' tattoos, 'n' sounds. Layers of players and more than a few nay-sayers. Some drunken pals. Some suffering gals. Winners and losers. Lots of boozers. Just a Friday night in Austin.

Like it is every Friday night at the Broken Spoke, 'n' who would want to be anywhere else?

I swear I do not EVER look for Dame Adventure. I do not WANT Dame Adventure!

I have a deviated septum, a Collies Fracture and trashed knees—and do not NEED more adventure, or broken bones or bottles thrown my way.

I was just there to dance. 'Cause I like to dance and what I said. Hold a pretty woman real close, right hand on her lower back. Slow-Quick-Quick; Slow-Quick-Quick. Say a word or two. Ask her name. Concentrate on the dance moves. Step back and twirl her, catch her eye and smile, real polite like. Asymmetrical is fine. Rinse with a cold Lone Star.

But the thing about Dame Adventure is that she whispers. Honest to God, she WHISPERS!

It's like you hear someone calling your name but it would be absolutely impossible to be boot-scootin' and hear a whisper when the band is playing Hank Jr.'s *Family Tra-dition!* But, there it was.

So, I began cutting 'round and side stepping and scanning the tables at the edge of the dance floor and made a full circle around the room.

Where in the WORLD did that whisper come from? WHO in the world is whispering my name? I just had ta' find out. Had ta'. Kin ya blame me?

It was like I was Moses and the redneck sea water parted and there She sat.

Right there at the end of the table. I was certain she whispered. She had a coy, knowing look in her eyes.

Her mother, about my age, sat beside her. Her mother was no rodeo rookie, Dolly hair, a flouncy, low-scooped blouse, bare-midriff, skin-tight jeans and a tooled belt which read "BITCH" 'n' Botox lips, ultra-glossy lipstick. I guessed dentures and defenses. On the table in front of her was a small clutch. My guess—a two-shot derringer.

This was the third time in my life that Dame Adventure brought me such a She. But, this time, She sat next to Her.

Her was the mother of She. She was a Dame Adventure gal who projected that adventuresome electro-magnetic, cardiac torus—that heart force field that had tingled my tangle and whispered to me.

I felt whatever in me that was solid turn to liquid and whatever was liquid turn to lust. My heart started racing. Other men sensed the adventuresome torus and started to look, too. My chest trembled. I smelled competition.

I stopped. Still.

My dance partner didn't know what was going on, but she followed my eyes and saw they were riveted on She, the one for me. I had to have her. I didn't know what it would take. Divorce, been there done that twice, no problem. Money, problem. Bass boat, well; but that didn't matter. With my tangle tingling like this, I didn't care about what it was going to cost.

She was just the most perfect woman. A wild abundance of sunlight and femaleness glowed around her. Young, fresh, untapped, spontaneous, pumping out that torus electro-magnetic tingly vibrations, waiting for me and my decisive move.

I was certain I had that old certainty.

But, dang!

The Hoary Astrological Planet Saturn, the God of Wisdom, kicked Macho Mars out of the way and showered me with historical memory forces. "This is your third perfect She!" Ol' man Saturn said. "Want me to remind you how the other two ended?" (I didn't want to admit it, but I already knew how this was going to end.) I touched my deviated septum. "Why do I always wind up with losers like She?" I asked the Hoary Astrological Planet Mars, the God of War. "If you don't take action now, bubba," said the God of War, "losers weepers!"

Double dang!

"Excuse me, Ma'am." I said to Her mother. "Would you like to dance?"

Her eyes lit up, her Botox levitated, she popped up, slung the tiny derringer clutch over her low-scoop flouncy blouse and held out her hand.

I kept tellin' myself, I was just there to dance. Hold a woman real close, right hand on her lower back. Slow-Quick-Quick; Slow-Quick-Quick... Say a word or two. Ask her name. (Mmm, she smells NICE.) Concentrate on the dance moves. Step back and twirl her, catch her eye and smile, real polite like. Asymmetrical is fine, but she really doesn't have much of an adipose tissue issue!

As we say in Texas: "It's better to aim at a star and hit a stump than aim at a stump and miss." That's the ol' certainty.

John Hunter, like the character in his story, has a "thang" about The Broken Spoke honky-tonk in Austin, Texas, and has spent many hours there. He also has a "thang" about country western music, boot scootin' and cold beer. Like the character in his story, John has a deviated septum. He also wishes that some day, Dame Adventure will put her arm around him. In real life, he is involved with organic agriculture and restorative justice.

Words and When I Knew Them

NANCY MEYER

Honorable Mention

1954 Age 11
Up your giggy with a meat hook, she slings,
sprawled on our bunks at Sunset Ranch Camp
spewing the worst words we knew.
All the girls gasp.
Metal hook, was her father a butcher?
Up where?

2017 Age 74
I finally looked: thumb and finger
the hook, 63 years a mystery
but her snarl never left me,
like the tough whispers
of my friend Sharon whose father
raped her every night.

1964 Age 21
Lunch, my place?
Bill Clay feeds me in his sunny kitchen, leads me
to the darkened bedroom a few kisses *oh no* I think

pushes me down on the double bed *No!* I say
knees squirm push with my free arm
pins my shoulders no condom *don't worry*
I'll pull out—
rush to the bathroom can't wash him out.
I, blonde Smithie, registering voters in Roxbury
he, lanky Black Nationalist guy in charge.
Walk back to work with him under rows of trees
imagining what we could be together.

> 1980 Age 37
> Nooner, said with a wink, from a friend
> sneaking off with her husband. Was that
> what Bill meant?

1964 Age 21
Why didn't I guess,
fight harder, why didn't I yell, run?
All to fit in. I let him in. *I* did it.

> 1990 Age 47
> The real word, Date Rape not even coined until 1973.
> In a woman's group, 26 years after that lunch
> first time I think it applies to me.
> No winks. *He* did it, not me.
> Not promiscuous-non-virgin-me.
> Still, only date rape. Not like Sharon's father.

1964 Age 21
Doctor looks up from between my legs. *Florence Crittendon Home for Unwed Mothers.*

> Right away, I know what this means.
> *Those* girls in high school who disappeared
> without a word.

1964 Age 21
2 ½ months. *Abortion now,* Dad urges. *Why didn't you tell us?*
Philly doc jailed; Puerto Rico clinics shut down for elections,

Japan out of reach. Tijuana a random tip.
San Diego Airport, beat-up car slithers through the dark,
nod and a few bills at the border. How often does he do this?
Sleazy motel. *Don't eat, I'll get you in A.M.*
Wait in his car, girls in white giggle down the sidewalk
    to First Communion.
You're next, past coughing kids to doctor in back.
$500 up front. But I already paid the driver.
Do you want it or not!
Twilight anesthesia; is this room even sterile?
Sick in Recovery, rows of us; *hurry up we need your bed.*
    Am I bleeding?
Woman next to me offers a ride to Anaheim. Her 3rd time.
Back at my New York job on Monday

1993 Age 50
Abortion, abortion mill rattled off my tongue
for years, a certain pride. Only when others
sat with me, wrapped my story in tissue paper,
handed my words back to me
tied with silk and listening did I sob all night
for this baby, for my young self.

2017 Age 74
Words alone: dry as a knife.

Nancy L. Meyer, who lives in the San Francisco Bay Area, is an avid cyclist, End of Life Counselor, and grandmother of five. Journals in which she has published include: *Colorado Review, Tupelo Quarterly, Bitterzoet, Poet's Touchstone, Wordland 6, Kneel Downe's Stolen Indie, Persimmon Tree, Kind of a Hurricane Press, Indolent Press, The Centrifugal Eye, The Sand Hill Review, Caesura, Snapdragon,* and *Passager.* Her work has appeared in eight anthologies, including *Open Hands* (Tupelo Press) and *Torch Song for Nelson Mandela* (Cherry Castle Publishing).

Aging

Brenda Mutchnik

Honorable Mention

I HAVE MADE A CONSCIOUS DECISION TO AGE WITH GRACE and dignity. No plastic surgery. No Botox. No liposuction. These will not be part of my later years. I would be thrilled if I could add vanity to the list, but she still continues to rear her head every morning as I walk past the mirror in the bedroom and gaze up as I dutifully brush my teeth. She even sneers at me when I enter the mirrored elevator in my building. It is my hope to soon replace vanity with pride.

In my younger days, a Rubenesque figure aka "zaftig" was appealing. Now it's just called dowdy. Photographs are painful. Cell phone videos, Facebook pictures and Skyping should be banned by any persons over the age of 75. I am totally convinced that a good deal of this new technology was developed as part of a conspiracy towards a much older version of the self that I once recognized as me. Yoga, palates and the plethora of creams in my bathroom cabinet don't begin to take away the wrinkles or that loose skin better known as "Hadassah Arms," which peeks out if the length of the sleeves on my shirts aren't correctly measured. And oh how I miss that beautiful décolletage, of which I was so proud for so many years.

A magnificent pair of Dolce Gabana, black silk flowered 4-inch heels currently reside comfortably at the top of my closet. Periodically, I get them down, dust them off and slip them onto my feet as if I were the Cinderella they have been waiting for. But what a disappointment to both the shoes and me when we sadly discover that I now have the stepsister's widened feet with nasty bunions that somehow appeared out of nowhere which prevent those beautiful babies from ever leaving their home on the very top shelf of the closet.

I was in Chicago on a very cold day recently, and found myself in a situation where I had to run to catch the last bus that would get me to my appointment. I looked at the bus and looked at the corner bus stop and mathematically figured out that if I ran, I could be at the corner in time to get the bus. My feet were pointed in the right direction but my legs didn't seem to understand the concept of running anymore. They stiffened. They stirred. I began to move forward. But no sprinting occurred. No long sylph-like steps were happening. Just a lot of huffing, puffing, and waddling in order to get to the corner. Aging!

I have deep admiration and a growing empathy for the Tin Man as he patiently waited for his oilcan. For me, it's become the hot shower that enables all my parts to get moving freely again.

Words, on the other hand, tend to take a vacation from their natural habitat inside my brain, while I'm in the middle of a sentence. They eventually come back home again in a few minutes . . . or at their naughtiest, a couple of hours. But there are times when they don't return until 2 or 3 A.M. and wake me from a blissful sleep. To make matters even worse, this embarrassing phenomenon has been saddled with the name "senior moment." Thank you very much, but I really don't need to be reminded.

I have finally accepted the fact that I shall never be tall. My hair will never be straight. My thighs will always be hefty. My eyes will always be brown. But I will continue to laugh. I will continue to learn. I will revel in my children's successes and comfort them in their failures. My instincts will remain intact. I will delight in discovering bits of myself in each of my grandchildren. And, if all goes well, I will continue to age.

Brenda Mutchnick lost her husband in 1974, and moved with her two young sons from Chicago to California, where she joined Paramount Pictures and then 20th Century Fox. She founded Rooster Entertainment in 1998, developing marketing materials for major motion picture, television, cable, video and corporate clients. Her first children's book, *A Noteworthy Tale,* was published by Abrams Books and translated into three languages. She has lectured on television, film and video marketing at UCLA, USC and Fordham University and is an active member of the Academy of Motion Picture Arts and Sciences. She currently resides in Beverly Hills while working on a book of essays covering subject matter from childhood to career to lovers to marriage to aging.

The Crux

Tank Gunner

Honorable Mention

THE CELEBRATION WAS OVER. THEY SAT IN A BOOTH AT Denny's waiting for their order, just the two of them. Convenience was the only reason they chose this lowly place, otherwise they would never think about passing through the doors of a chain restaurant. A Denny's, of all places. Even an IHOP would be a better selection.

The place was packed. Patrons, still in a joyful, loud, boisterous mood at two in the morning of this New Year, poured in for a blue-plate breakfast special to absorb the abundant champagne. Groups of revelers still enjoyed the merriment of the moment.

It was hard to hear, even harder for Maureen to listen to Shirley go on and on about the Rolex Toby gave her as an anniversary present. All damn night she boasted how well Toby treated her: the BMW he gave, the Italian villa, a condo on the Riviera beach, his 747 always available, even Chipper, the cute puppy she cherished which Toby called a "Shit Sue." Now, added to her collection was the $18,000 diamond Rolex.

Shirley was a multi-millionaire in her own right. After two years at Panola Junior College, she created her own international conglomerate and served as CEO for 40 years. She didn't need or want Toby's money or gifts, but she did enjoy his attention. Everything he gave she gave to her charity, except this Rolex.

Frankly, Maureen, Shirley's advisor, confidant, consultant, and best friend, had had it up to her pencil-lined, mascara painted eyebrows. The Rolex was the crux; maybe the New Year's Eve flow of martinis and champagne fueled Maureen's envy.

Since fourth grade, when both were 10, Maureen played second fiddle to Shirley. Always, it was Shirley this, Shirley that, and Shirley don't cha know. At noon yesterday, Maureen began thinking of a way to diminish the wind in Shirley's sail. She didn't know why meanness was brewing in her heart; she had no answer if asked. Maureen had no clue why she decided the Rolex was her target.

Maureen loved Shirley. She loved that Shirley was her best friend, and loved being Shirley's best friend, for all these decades. They had their weddings together, in Shirley's church. Their husbands died within weeks of each other. They had grieved together and supported each other in the aftermath. They had never argued, never fought.

Even though Shirley sometimes could be a boastful braggart, she had never ever treated Maureen badly or shabbily. These past 48 years, after both received advanced degrees at age 20 with top honors in business and social sciences, Maureen worked with Shirley, never for her. Every year they went on extravagant sojourns. Shirley always paid; she footed the bill, whatever the cost. Didn't matter. She paid for all their pleasurable outings.

The most memorable jaunts were to Hong Kong, for a month-long vacation. They flew on the Concorde to Paris where they vacationed for an entire summer, twice. Four years in a row, they enjoyed Oktoberfest in Munich. Skiing in the Swiss Alps included a weekend diversion to the Vatican. Shirley's business connections arranged an introduction to the Pope.

A two-week vacation in the Australian outback included a weekend break to fly over to Queensland, New Zealand, to jump 900 meters off the bridge where A. J. Hackett invented the sport of Bungee jumping.

There were parachute jumps and soaring glider flights. They used a helicopter, of course, to climb Mount Everest and Mount Kilimanjaro.

Quick trips, multiple times, to mainline China, India, Africa, the Middle East, the Himalayas, Russia, Mexico, Canada, and Texas.

There were side trips, after business meetings, maybe even two or three a year, to unknown and uncharted pieces of earth. Shirley would buy tickets for both of them to travel to outer space if it was possible.

Now, tonight, this morning, Maureen had enough. She would not be able to explain why it was even in her head to go after the Rolex. Shirley was her best friend, and always had been. In all the happy moments and all the sad events, they were there for each other, as best friends always are and should be.

Both were attracted to Toby when he came into their lives. At 74, he was six years older. Even though both felt energetic and active, Toby made them feel 30 again, sexy, awakened, and alive.

Nevertheless, as it turned out, Toby favored Shirley. There was no jealousy, no staking of a claim, no secrecy, and certainly no attempt to go from a trio to a duo. Shirley made sure of that, never excluding Maureen from Toby's attention. Toby seemed to enjoy the threesome as much as Shirley did.

Now, the Rolex burned in Maureen's head. Why she wanted it was a complete mystery. To take it, she knew, was thievery. Maureen knew she had to have it. She would be miserable without it.

How could she get it? She had no plan to make it happen. Her desire was unexplainable, her motivation uncharacteristic. It just was not Maureen's nature to covet another's property. It, indeed, was a conundrum.

The shotgun blast into the ceiling stunned the dozens of breakfast diners. It was a dramatic tactic to gain complete attention for the strategic announcement.

"Don't nobody fuckin move!"

Five bandits dressed in black ski masks and black overcoats stood at the entrance. Two were short, women obvious to the eye, even heavily garbed in black. Two men had sawed-off, pump shotguns, and the third man held a machine pistol loaded with a long magazine.

In the deafening silence, in the still quietness, not a coffee cup clacked or an ice cube clinked. Nobody coughed, burped, or farted. Everybody was breathless, wary, and afraid. Throughout the restaurant, hearts pounded, veins pulsed. One of the women robbers stepped up on a vacant chair and mounted a tabletop. She held an AK-47, its sling draped over her right shoulder. Her view of Denny's interior was inclusive.

"Put your money and your jewelry in the hat, all of it. I'll kill any son-of-a-bitch who fucks around. Do it now!" Her voice was stern, firm, convincing. With small steps, she turned 360 degrees on the tabletop, the automatic rifle barrel leveled at faces and bodies. Only her green eyes and bright, purple painted lips were visible.

The other woman, and a man with a shotgun, produced a pop-out top hat. They started on opposite sides of the dining area, working the room, passing the hat.

Shirley shoved her coat off the booth's bench onto the floor.

When Shirley removed her diamond necklace, diamond rings, diamond bracelet, and the Rolex, Maureen formed her plan.

The bandit's coat smelled like marijuana smoke and mothballs. He shoved the hat at Shirley who dropped her cash, diamonds, and the Rolex in it.

Instead of dropping her silver costume ring with an ersatz diamond setting and her Timex into the hat, Maureen reached over and laid her possessions in.

At the very moment of implementing her plan, the bandit with the machine pistol at the door created the lucky distraction.

"Don't you fuckin' move again, asshole, I'll blow your goddam head off!"

Turning away for an instant, the hat holder looked in the direction of his yelling partner.

According to plan, Maureen palmed the Rolex. She withdrew her hand with it in it, and placed both hands on her lap below the tabletop. She kept her head down. The bandit with the hat paid no attention to Maureen's ploy and moved to the next booth.

As swift as it started, the robbery was over. Through large front windows, victims watched bandits rush out to a red, four-door sedan and pile in. The car sped away.

Patrons stampeded through the door, spilling into the parking area. Even cooks, table cleaners, and wait staff ran out. Denny's now was empty, except for the two best friends.

"Maureen. Maureen, are you all right?"

"I'm terrified, but I'm okay." Maureen bent forward. Under the tabletop, she raised her dress, and stuck the Rolex under the waistband of her panties. "I thought I would pee in my pants. I think I need to go before I do."

"Me, too, Maureen, in just a second, Honey." Shirley pulled her mink coat from the floor and reached into the left pocket. This movement stirred the Chanel embedded in the fabric and the fur. She withdrew her hand from the pocket and held out a slim, long white box tied with a red ribbon. "I am so glad I waited to give this to you, sweetheart. I love you."

Maureen took the present, untied the ribbon, and removed the lid from the box. A sparkling, diamond studded Rolex lay undisturbed in its crib.

It was identical to the $18,000 Rolex Shirley dropped into the bandit's hat, and was now pressing on Maureen's waist.

Now, Maureen really needed to pee.

"I know you admired the Rolex Toby gave me, so I bought one for you. This is for my one and only best friend forever. Thank you for being my friend, Maureen. Since fourth grade, I have always loved you, and I always will. Happy New Year, Darling."

Maureen raised her head and looked into her very best friend's bright, smiling, loving face.

As shame and despair flooded her heart, tears spilled from Maureen's eyes and slid down her cheeks.

"Oh, my god." Maureen shook her head with slight movement. Her voice was a soft whisper. "Oh, sweet Jesus."

Tank Gunner is the pen name of a retired combat cavalry trooper, senior parachutist, and jumpmaster. He has been awarded a Combat Infantry Badge and decorated with a Silver Star, a Purple Heart, and three Bronze Stars, one for valor. He served his nation with pride and honor for more than a quarter century as an enlisted soldier and officer. Tank's third book, *Cookie Johnson,* follows his contributions to the anthologies *Prompts* and *Prompts Too,* which are filled with entertaining and engaging short stories written in his superb style. He and his wife live near Dallas with Toby.

Summer of '61

Joe Crawford

Honorable Mention

IN THE INFORMATION AGE, APHORISMS ARE RARELY HEARD. Half a 100 years ago, they were frequently voiced by people of all walks of life. Urbane academics and blunt talking rural horse traders alike delighted in enlightening others with their favorite words of wisdom. Contrition-free, they'd proudly spit out their sage saying like it was Kentucky Twist chewing tobacco juice.

Back then, one aphorism became all too real to me, a farm boy from down on Mill Creek. The guilt and pain still lingers and the wound won't heal.

"What's the matter with that mare?" Dad asked Joe Williams, the tri-state area's visiting veterinarian.

"Her wind's busted, Carl. Been rode hard and put up wet. She may have a touch of colic, too."

"Is she going to die? Lordy, I hope not! She's sold. A fella over at Farner's already paid me for her. I was supposed to deliver her today."

Near the mare's head, Doc Williams squatted down and with both hands reached toward the downed mare's mouth, he parted her lips. Mumbling to himself, he counted her black-streaked teeth and side-glanced at their angle. Slowly rising from his hunkered position, he stepped back, looked knowingly into the hayloft and said, "She most likely won't ever get up. If you take ropes and pulleys and lift her to her feet, sometimes a busted horse will recover, but her odds aren't good. She's old."

Hidden behind bales of hay, we three boys strained to hear Doc's gloomy prognosis. Peeking down from our hayloft perch, my older brother, Jim, our neighbor friend T-Bone Watkins, and I had studied Doc's every move. He meticulously checked the vital signs of the slow-dying equine. In the silence of the dusty, light-starved barn, Doc's dismal words cut like a knife. Old Doc Williams knew we were up there in the loft, but mercifully he kept mum to Dad about our whereabouts.

I remember the mare well. I recall her head, neck, and gaunt, gun-barrel trunk looking as though they were glued to the ground. Her eyes were wide opened, teary, and her eyelashes were crusted. And that blank stare; the stare acknowledging nothing, not even the flies that buzzed above her noble head and crawled around the perimeter of her eyelids. I can see the splayed illumination—the columns of sunlight that filtered through the barn's cracks, placing odd-shaped spots on her entire body. I remember her feeble groans.

It was a typical summer day, mid-July and mid-morning. Hot and hazy, cottony clouds hovered. Eye-high corn had been laid by. Work around the farm was lax. Few chores demanded our time. All work animals had been turned out, each jumping, kicking high, and gyrating herky-jerky body movements before flat-out sprinting from the barn like jail break convicts. Freedom! They'd now fend for themselves, forage for food from the field and woods until about fall frost time. Except her, the aging bay mare that lay lifeless on her side.

And there we were, three May-morn boys, fresh, green, acting older than we really were. There are the culprits, two of us gripped by guilt, masking remorse, sharing shame. There we were flinching in unison, as though harnessed together, each time she made her soul-stirring groan.

And there were the artifacts: our attempts to make it right with her and console our guilty conscience, but all to no avail. There was the tangible evidence of our efforts, the comfort articles, appearing almost as though on display: There was the finely crushed corn, the oat hay, and the shiny steel water bucket with condensate trickling down its outside.

Sunday—July 10, 1961

We boys had felt no ill will toward the old mare. We were simply indifferent to her. We didn't know her age or her physical condition. All we knew was that we were tired of our boredom that Sunday afternoon. We wanted some excitement, something to fight the everyday humdrum of farm life. She was a horse—the vehicle of every cowboy star on the big screen and TV, the essential item for an adventuresome life. She would serve as an implement for our Sunday fantasy, our little diversion from reality. It all started so innocently, but ended so wrong.

Down on Mill Creek after church and dinner, Jim, T-Bone, and I were doing nothing. We were just sprawled out on the front porch, swatting flies, telling lies, and watching the yard birds pecking the ground when out of nowhere a city boy from McCaysville by name of Jerry Duke sauntered up. We all knew Jerry from school to be mouthy, bossy. Jerry said, "What's you feller's doing?"

Jim looked up and curtly told Jerry, "Nothing. We're doing nothing, Duke. Try it sometime. You'll like it."

"Well, not me! I want to have some fun," fired back Jerry. Then Jerry proclaimed, "Hey! I've got a super idea. Why don't we go ride y'alls horses? I know full well y'all got horses. Your dad's a horse trader. See him driving his truck through town all the time with horses on it. Come on guys! It'd be a blast! Let's do it. More fun than hanging here."

"We don't have any horses, Jerry. Dad sold them all," was Jim's surly retort. Then, correcting his words, he says, "Well, not all. We got that one old mare locked up in the stable, but she ain't really ours anymore. Dad sold her. He's hauling her to her new home in Farner, Tennessee, tomorrow. Besides, she's just an old plow horse. No good for riding. She's not a saddle horse." Then Jim flashed a you-bug-me, get-lost creep, eyeball at Jerry.

"We could ride her anyway, couldn't we?" fired back Jerry.

"I suppose, but wouldn't be much fun. Someone would have to walk. All four of us wouldn't fit on her and couldn't all ride her at once."

"Sounds like more fun than staying here on the porch the rest of the day," I burst out with confident defiance. "Let's do it. Let's go get that old mare and ride The Old Epworth Road. Let's go over to the school playground. Might be a softball game going on."

"Let's do it guys. What you say?"

"Well, count me out," Jim snapped. "I'm staying here. Don't care nothing about riding no stupid plow horse." He then rose up, sneered at Jerry, and went in the house, the screen door tensioned by a long spiral spring banging him in the butt as he entered.

Lazily, and saying nothing, T-bone followed Jerry and me to the barn. I bridled and led the old mare out from the dingy stable into the midday sun. Standing beside her, I jumped high, caught hold of her mane, pulled myself up and straddled the plow horse. Blasé, she bobbed her head once, but otherwise didn't move a muscle.

I took the reins in hand, clucked my tongue, and with the heel of my PF Flyers goosed her in the ribs. She ambled over to an embankment. There, behind me, Jerry, then T-Bone, climbed aboard the bareback sluggish old steed.

"Get up, horse," I screamed with glee and then I made a clicking sound. Gravel crunching underfoot. Down the hill and off toward the Old Epworth Road she moseyed.

We had just reached it when Jerry protested: "Is this as fast as she can go? We'll be midnight getting to the ball field if this old nag don't speed up. Goose it."

I goosed her in the side. She broke into a slow trot. Up and down, bouncing around and hanging on to each other, we three riders struggled to stay upright and aboard.

"Make her gallop! Make her gallop! It's a more fun ride," Jerry demanded.

I goosed her again. She slow trotted into a quirky canter. For a short while the ride was smooth, but then the road inclined. She started wheezing and her gate fell back to a trot. We three riders repeated our bouncing about, clinging to each other, struggling to stay aboard.

"Goose her again! Go faster," like a marine drill instructor, Jerry ordered. I complied. She broke into a gallop. This time she ran a little faster. Her gate was smoother. Up hills, and down hills and through sandy, sun bathed ruts she plodded along like a freight train.

Her brown slick coat turned wet and burgundy in color. White lather formed where the bridle reins rubbed her neck. She sweated profusely. Huffing and puffing hard, like a Mac semi-truck, she maintained her steady pace. In less than 30 minutes she had traversed three miles to the Epworth baseball field.

Impatiently, we disembarked the old beast, threw down the reins, and left her to her leisure. We stretched and readjusted the crotch of our sweat-soaked Wranglers. She snorted once, lowered her head and nonchalantly began grazing in the high grass of the baseball outfield.

Open hands shielding sun from his eyes, Jerry surveyed the abandoned field. He grumbled, "Well, dang it! Ain't nobody here. I's hoping we'd get a little game going, but everybody's gone. Where is everybody?"

From his front pocket, T-Bone pulled out a bag of STUD smoking tobacco. He untied its strings and fingered the loose leafs. Pouring the tobacco onto white smoke paper, he voiced his first words of the trip: "Fine by me. I don't care diddly-squat 'bout playin' ball in this hot sun. Think I'll get me a shot of water." He licked the rolled cigarette and stuck it between his lips. Then he struck a match on his Wrangler's zipper, lit and short-puffed his rolled smoke. He strolled over to the spring. Holding the cigarette at his side, he ladled two dippers of water.

Jerry complained again, "Well, let's get back. This place is Deadsville. Ain't nothing happening here. We need to find something fun to do. Maybe we can go fishing down at the Maple Hole. Now where'd that old nag go to?"

The old mare had taken cover in the shade of a tree at the end of the outfield. Head down, she gasped for air, as her tail swatted flies. Oddly, her sweating had not stopped. Lightning quick, three riders were aboard. T-Bone cautioned me, "Better go slow, Joe. Somethin's a matter with that old mare. Hear her breathing? I'm telling ya, she ain't right."

I ignored T-Bone. I goosed her in the ribs, hoping for an even faster trip to the Maple Hole. Huffing and puffing and still sweating, she was on her way. Like a loyal combatant, she soldiered on. She delivered us to Mill Creek and the Maple Hole located about two miles away. Off her we three riders descended. We stood and stared into the cool deep waters of the slow meandering stream.

I thought to myself, *Forget about fishing. It's hot. We should go swimming!*

"Hey fellers," I shouted. "Let's go swimming. Last one in is a rotten egg!" Laughing and picking and poking at each other, we three shed our clothes. Jaybird, we plunged into the Maple Hole. We left the old mare unattended.

She found her way down the creek to a place where the water was wide but shallow. There she guzzled down water, swilling long draws for about 10 minutes. With more than her fill of cold creek water, the old mare took immediate refuge in the shade of a nearby maple. From our vantage point we couldn't see her, but heard her wheezing. Caught up in our swimming and frolicking, we were soon unconscious of her existence.

Later, we lay in the sun on a large flint rock, warming and drying off. Then we got clothed. We located the old sweaty, wheezy beast and rode her back to the barn. This time we didn't make her gallop. T-Bone didn't ride her. Instead, he walked along beside her.

Nearing home, without warning, Jerry slid off the rear of the old mare. Landing on his feet, he broke out in a slow-trot away from us. He looked over his shoulder and said, "I got to cut out. See you clowns in the funny papers." Heads down, T-Bone and I didn't respond.

Arriving at the barn, I promptly put her in her stable. T-Bone waited outside the barn. When I returned he asked me, "Do you need me to help you feed and water that mare?"

"No, I'll take care of that later. Hope mom's got supper on the table. I'm starved. Come eat with us, T-Bone."

"No. Gotta get on home. I got some chores to do 'fore dark. See you later."

T-Bone slipped away home. Sundown came.

Monday—July 11, 1961

That morning when I went to feed and water the old mare, I found her partially down. She appeared to be stuck in a half up and half down position. Her front feet were on the ground, but her rear wouldn't budge. Her breathing was still wheezy and she didn't respond to touch. Lunging forward, and trying hard, she could not get up. Later, spent from her efforts, she lay her head down. I knew then she was terribly sick. That's when the guilt and anxiety hit me.

I remember having mixed feelings about what to do next: Better get my older brother, Jim. He'll know what to do. No, can't let him know. If I do, he'll think he knows more than me about horses. Oh, dear God! What should I do? Could it be that us boys riding her yesterday made her sick? She can't get up. Maybe I'm to blame. You're stupid, Joe Snothead! Only one thing you can do now: Pray to God she gets well. And, you gotta tell Dad. You gotta tell him what you did.

Tuesday—July 12, 1961

There she was, stiff as a 10-penny nail, all four legs extended. There she was not wheezing anymore. There she was looking out from those glazed over brown eyes, but seeing nothing or no one for evermore. There she was, being pulled with a tractor to her grave. There she was, in her grave, being pelted and covered with clods of red dirt.

Wednesday—July 13, 1961

There we were, Dad and me at daybreak, like two whipped puppies standing on the front porch of the dead horse's owner. There he was, the owner, dressed in bib overalls with one buckle hanging down, picking a piece of pork from his teeth as he opened the screened door and greeted us. There he was, suddenly silent, looking at Dad, then at me, and then back at Dad again, sensing something's awry. There he was, asking the question that still haunts me and rattles about inside my now graying head:

"Did you bring me my mare, Carl? I got me some plowing to do today."

There I was jittery, chin trembling, shoulders shaking. There I was, confusing the man, babbling jumbled jabber, saying something about killing his horse. There I was bursting into tears. There I was looking up to Dad, wet eyes pleading for him to explain to the man what happened. There I was a disgrace and prime example of everyone's favorite aphorism:

"Some people will ride a good horse to death."

I did it. I rode a man's good horse to death. It's a wound that won't ever heal.

There he was, my Dad getting ready to deliver his persuasive pitch. There he was, explaining and apologizing to the man, telling him that his horse had mysteriously become sick and died. There he was cutting a new deal, offering to get the man another plow horse at half the price. There they were shaking on the agreement.

There was the man from Farner, Tennessee, smiling, tousling my hair, telling me "it couldn't be helped son; forget about it; animals die." There he was in my young damp eyes back then, and there he is still today, in my aged dry eyes, the most merciful man in the state of Tennessee.

Fifty-five summers have come and gone since the old mare died. The events surrounding her death changed me, a precocious farm boy seeking to impress his peers. From her dying, I learned that insensitivity and inaction on moral issues have consequences. It was one of many character development opportunities I was privileged to encounter down on Mill Creek.

Joe Cobb Crawford is a retired electrical engineer. His career as an author began in 2010 with a memoir entitled *The Poetry Company: Memoirs of a Chicken Catcher*. He honed his writing skills by attending several courses from The University of Iowa's Summer Writing Festival. The characters and setting for his writings are from yesteryear Appalachia. In 2015, he self-published a murder mystery, *The Lies We Bury,* that gained him recognition as a writer of the year candidate by the Georgia Writers Association. He's a native of Blue Ridge, Georgia, and lives with his wife, Susan, on Lake Hartwell.

An Arrested Development

Terri Elders

Recognized

I'M NO SAINT, BUT I'VE LED AN UPSTANDING LIFE. I'VE BEEN a high school teacher, a psychiatric social worker, a Peace Corps volunteer, a wife (twice) and a mother (once). I've worked for federal, state and municipal governments and as a local contractor for three years for a foreign republic. Even in retirement, I serve on boards, councils and commissions. You'd probably regard me as a pillar of the community, a poster child for civility.

So you'd never suspect that I'm a criminal who spent a night behind bars.

When newscasts feature police wrestling along suspects in what's become known as a perp walk, I start to shiver. *Been there, done that,* I think, rubbing my forearms to quell the persistent goose bumps. Time does not heal all wounds. I know. It's been over 50 years since I found my law-abiding self literally crossing the line, yet I still shudder when I think about getting arrested.

That night so many years ago when my husband and I set off for a Christmas party the evening before Christmas Eve, which we jokingly alluded to as Christmas Eve-Eve, we looked forward to downing a few screwdrivers, trading tall tales with Bob's fellow police officers and ending our excursion with a midnight feast of steak and eggs at

Hody's Drive-in. That was the pattern we usually followed on our rare nights out.

Bob had worked as a patrolman on what the Long Beach Police Department then called the "early three" shift, 3 P.M. to 11 P.M., for the two and a half years he'd been on the force. With little seniority, he also worked on weekends. So on December 23, 1958, we took our 10-month-old son to Bob's parents' home for a sleepover and set off for the party. We weren't whistling Christmas carols, but we certainly felt infused with holiday spirit.

"It's not too bad having Tuesdays and Wednesdays off," Bob remarked, maneuvering our old Pontiac into a tight parking space on the palm-tree-lined suburban street. "At least this year we can go to a party, have Christmas Eve lunch with my folks and laze around Christmas morning before I have to go back to work Thursday afternoon."

"True. It worked out pretty well this year," I agreed. "We'll have our Christmas dinner before you leave. The turkey's small enough that I won't have to get up too early Christmas morning to get it in the oven."

Once in a while we discussed how nice it might be if Bob worked day shifts and enjoyed weekends off, a more traditional lifestyle. I hoped that once our son was in school, Bob could get assigned to days. But privately, I actually enjoyed having him out of the house on weekend afternoons. As soon as he'd leave, I'd plop the baby down for a nap and pick up a book. I was a junior that year, majoring in English at Long Beach State College, carrying some tough literature courses that required a lot of reading and writing. When Bob was home, he'd watch *I Love Lucy* reruns and quiz shows, and in our little two-bedroom house, even in the bedroom with the door closed, I could hear the blare. I longed to set up my portable Smith-Corona on the dining room table, but had to settle for tapping away while sitting cross-legged on the bed.

What a great break for us to have a night out, I thought again, as we entered our host's house. The living room was packed with guests, so it took us some time to greet friends and weave our way around the Christmas tree to get to the kitchen, where Bob set a quart of orange juice and fifth of vodka on the counter. In those "bring your own bottle" days, we always drank screwdrivers. Because I didn't much enjoy the acrid taste of vodka, I always took mine pretty light. But I'd started to notice that Bob skimped on the O.J. when he mixed his own drinks.

Clutching our highballs, we returned to the living room. I joined a group of women on a sofa, and Bob huddled with some buddies in a corner. In the late '50s, the sexes rarely mingled at cop parties. The guys talked shop and exchanged risqué jokes. The gals discussed babies and recipes for clam dip or pecan sandies. In those days, few policemen's wives worked. The men still believed it a disgrace to their manhood if they weren't singlehandedly supporting their family.

When Bob shared the news that I intended to become a high school English teacher, his friends would shake their heads. "I'd never let my wife work," they would say. "It's terrible for the kids."

"Well, my mom worked. She and dad were both nurses, and I grew up all right," my husband would reply.

So I wasn't surprised that evening that none of the women I sat with showed much interest in what I was reading in my literature courses, even though one or two did ask about my classes. I listened to the chatter about teething remedies and diaper rash, nodded and smiled, and every once in a while, bored to bits, wandered into the kitchen to replenish my drink.

Not long before midnight, Bob sidled over and jerked his head towards the bedroom where I'd stashed my purse and jacket.

"Let's head on out," he said. "Doc thinks it would be fun to drive down to Orange County to grab some breakfast at an all-night diner he likes down near Newport."

I hesitated. I could tell by the slight glaze in his eyes that Bob had put a big dent in the fifth of vodka.

"Do you think it's safe to leave Long Beach?"

Bob had told me more than one story about Long Beach police being pulled over by fellow officers and kicked loose as a courtesy. It seemed to be an unspoken code that a cop didn't write a DUI for a fellow cop.

"Sometimes we make a guy park his car and we'll give him a lift home. But we don't arrest each other," he explained.

"Hey, it's only about an hour away. I'm fine."

Then Doc approached. A burly man, probably a decade older than most of the officers there that night, Doc had a reputation for heavy boozing and womanizing. He was one of the few officers attending who'd not brought along his wife. Bob had mentioned earlier that Doc's wife didn't like parties. That never seemed to stop Doc from attending, and he'd usually be the only man in the room chatting with other men's wives, and flirtatiously, too.

"Let's go," he caroled. "I'm feeling full of the Christmas spirit tonight. Breakfast will be on me."

Bob winked at me. We knew we'd had barely enough left after buying our Christmas turkey to cover the cost of steak and eggs at Hody's. We liked Doc's offer to pick up the tab at a café likely to be costlier than our neighborhood drive-in.

So we took off, Bob behind the wheel, with Doc in the passenger seat, and me tucked into the cramped back seat of the old Plymouth. As we headed south, I began to get drowsy. Apparently I drifted off to sleep because the next thing I knew I could hear Bob arguing with somebody who didn't sound like Doc.

I opened my eyes and jerked my head around. We'd pulled into a service station.

"Bob's drunker than I thought," Doc whispered. "I noticed he was weaving when he went in to pay the attendant for the gas."

The service station attendant approached the car.

"I think this guy has had too much to drink," he said. "Can anybody else here take the wheel?"

I blinked, and shook my head. I still hadn't mastered a stick shift and didn't even have a driver's license.

"There's no problem," Bob insisted. "I can drive."

When Doc remained quiet, I realized he probably was drunk as well. I thought I'd heard a slight slur when he remarked about watching Bob walk.

The attendant grimaced and headed back to the station. We took off.

Five minutes later, as we neared the outskirts of Newport, I heard the wail of a siren, and swiveled my head around to face flashing lights.

Bob pulled the Plymouth to the side of the road. He and Doc traded stricken glances.

A pair of Orange County sheriffs approached and Bob rolled down his window.

"A service station attendant phoned and described a 1949 blue

Plymouth. He said he thought the driver was intoxicated. We're going to have to ask all of you to take some tests."

I was sober enough to realize I'd be asked to walk a straight line and perform other balancing tricks, like a trained seal. Edging out of the car, I realized that my boredom earlier in the evening had led me to the kitchen counter more times than I'd actually counted. I wasn't drunk, but I certainly was intoxicated. I began to explain this to the sheriff.

"I don't know how to drive a stick shift," I began, "Or I'd have taken the wheel."

Bob and Doc stared at me and shook their heads. I shut up.

I managed to walk heel-to-toe without wavering, but when I had to put my arms straight out and balance on my left foot, I swayed. My right foot thumped down before I toppled over. I'd flunked the test.

The three of us were booked at the Orange County jail. They charged Bob with driving under the influence, and Doc and me with "intoxicated in auto." I was herded into a tiny solitary cell.

"Great," I thought. "Now what? Will the guys lose their jobs? What about me? Will I ever get a school district to hire me now, with an arrest record?"

I curled up on my cot and fell asleep, waking often through the night to agonize over yet another issue. What would Bob's parents think if we didn't turn up by noon to pick up the baby? How would we afford to pay the fine? How would we make mortgage payments if Bob lost his job?

I glanced at my little Elgin that my parents had given me for my high school graduation. It was nearly 8 A.M. I was hungry. I remembered we'd been drinking on empty stomachs. We'd skipped dinner since we'd been saving our appetites for that midnight breakfast at Hody's.

A matron unlocked the door of my cell.

"Come along. Your husband and his friend are waiting in the lobby. You can wait there with them."

Bob and Doc glanced at me sheepishly. I realized I must have looked disgusted with them both.

"The bail bondsman will be here in a few minutes," Bob said. "We'll drop Doc off to pick up his car, and head for Downey to pick up the baby."

"We have to stop by the house first. Your parents will know something's wrong if we show up looking all wrinkled and disheveled, as if we'd slept in our clothes. Which we have."

So at least I got a quick shower and fresh clothes. But I couldn't wash away the overwhelming sense of dread that stayed with me as we struggled through the next few dismal days.

On Christmas morning I went through the motions of fixing a turkey dinner, but neither of us took much pleasure in eating it. This was the first time I'd seen my husband turn down seconds on candied sweet potatoes.

Bob and Doc hired a criminal defense attorney friendly to cops, a man known as The Silver Fox. He thought he could plea bargain and get Bob's charge reduced to reckless driving, if Doc and I both pled no contest to our charges.

"Just what is 'intoxicated in auto' and why is that a crime?" I'd asked.

The lawyer explained that in California at that time, public intoxication extended to being a passenger in any vehicle that is stopped, for no matter what reason.

"For instance, if you'd called a cab and the driver blew a red light, you could be arrested for public intoxication."

All I knew was that it sounded unfair. I'd been asleep in the back seat of a car that I didn't even know how to drive.

The ploy worked, though, and Bob kept his job.

Nonetheless, it was only the beginning of a series of humiliating incidents for me. For decades, every time I filled out a job application I had to explain that yes, I'd been arrested for a misdemeanor, and provide the lurid details.

In interviews I'd find myself blushing as I explained how I was asleep in the car after a Christmas party. Most employers were sympathetic, more so than what I'd expect them to be today, when laws are much more stringent about blood alcohol levels and what constitutes intoxication.

The chief damage, though, was to my marriage. I'd lost faith in Bob to exercise good judgment. I blamed him for the whole thing. I never accepted any responsibility in what happened that long ago holiday season. Instead for years I just seethed.

After 25 years of marriage, we divorced.

Bob's drinking had gradually spiraled out of control, and twice he was hospitalized with acute pancreatitis as a result. Eventually he entered an in-patient program, and remained sober for 22 years before he died of unrelated causes.

One day I decided to apply to become a Peace Corps Volunteer. I called Bob and asked if that misdemeanor was still on my record in California. I knew he could run a check. When he phoned back he was chuckling.

"I checked, and there's nothing. It's not there. I'm not certain it's ever been there. They may never have put it on your record in the first place."

All that agony for nothing, I thought, remembering my embarrassment and anxiety every time I switched jobs. All that blame and shame... for nothing. All that hostility and rage... for nothing.

Even so, I answered truthfully on the Peace Corps application. Yes, I'd been arrested. It really happened, whether it had been recorded or not. Peace Corps has the FBI do background checks on applicants. I certainly didn't want the FBI to say I'd lied. Besides, there might be some trace that Bob had overlooked.

The truth is... I've been busted.

Only now do I realize that I could have talked Bob out of driving to Newport that long ago December night, pleading a headache or a queasy tummy. I could have maneuvered him away from Doc with promises of late night kisses and cuddles. But I didn't. I let him drive, even knowing it was unsafe.

Instead, I went along willingly. And somebody could have been killed. There could have been a tragic outcome, something far more serious than merely my chagrin.

I'd been an accomplice. That's my real crime.

TERRI ELDERS, LCSW, is a lifelong writer and editor. In the past decade she began to write about her life's adventures. Now as she nears 81, she's thrilled that her stories have appeared in over a hundred anthologies, including multiple editions of *Chicken Soup for the Soul.* She's a co-creator for *Not Your Mother's Book,* an anthology series from Publishing Syndicate. Terri, who received the 2006 UCLA Alumni award for community service for her work internationally with the Peace Corps, served for eight years as a public member of the Washington State Medical Quality Assurance Commission. Contact her at telders@hotmail.com and read her blog http://atouchoftarragon.blogspot.com.

The Babe in the Box

Richard Perreault

Recognized

IF HADE PICKETT COULD FIND HIS WAY FROM FRUITION to the UPS Freight Center in Asheville in time for his 1:30 interview, he figured he stood a good chance of landing one of the coveted Christmas season jobs. The narrow, winding mountain roads of western Carolina were as familiar to Hade as the back of his hand; but the crowded, hill-bedeviled streets of Asheville, with their unfamiliar names and unforgiving drivers, were more like an open palm slap-in-the-face. Fortunately, Hade's neighbor, Dixie Hooper—who seemed to have a solution for every problem—had loaned him the GPS she'd gotten for Christmas the year before. He'd been reluctant at first to accept Dixie's offer, but the way he saw it, borrowing a contraption that gives directions from a woman wasn't the same as actually asking a woman *for* directions.

The morning of Hade's appointment, Dixie handed the little black box to her grandson, Bennie, so he could enter Hade's destination. She had never learned to use the gadget. "Onliest places I go are church and the grocery store," she'd told Hade. "Good Book tells me all I need to know about findin' Jesus, and I been makin' my own way to the Piggly Wiggly for better part of 30 years."

Hade watched Bennie jab at the buttons with the speed and delight of a chicken eating grubs. "Here," he said, handing the GPS to Hade. "When you get ready to turn it on, mash this button on top."

Hade turned the box over in his hand, studying its smooth plastic angles. "So, some satellite up in the sky is going to be watching me drive all the way to Asheville, telling me where I need to turn?"

"Most satellites are up in the sky," Bennie replied, with no attempt to mask the sarcasm.

"What if it clouds up and the satellite can't see me?" Hade asked.

Bennie closed his eyes; shook his head like he was rearranging something that had come loose in his brain. "Just do what it tells you and there's no way you can get lost."

Hade closed his meaty hand around the little box, thanked Dixie and Bennie, and headed out to his truck. He settled into the worn vinyl seat and set the GPS on the passenger side. He gripped the cracked plastic steering wheel and inhaled the ever-present mingling of petroleum smells that told the story of things that always leaked. If he got the UPS job he'd be able to afford one of those fancy leather steering wheel covers and maybe even replace a gasket or two. He reached for the GPS and pushed the *On* button like Bennie had told him to do.

Before he could turn the key to crank the engine, a soft female voice informed him she was *calculating*. Hade couldn't help but look to see if someone had snuck into the truck and sat down alongside him.

Again, the woman said, "Calculating."

"Never knew a woman who wasn't," Hade said, laughing because he'd already gotten one up on the babe in the box.

A picture of a toy car appeared on the gadget's screen. Hade pushed the GPS further across the seat. "You just keep your distance and everything'll be fine," he said, wanting to make it clear up front who was in charge.

"Drive point two miles, then turn right on Stink Dog Creek Road," the woman said.

"I know how to get out of Dixie Hooper's driveway," Hade groused. He could see taking directions from this woman wasn't going to be any picnic, but at least he wouldn't have to watch as she rolled her eyes and twisted her mouth into a smug pucker every time he made a wrong turn, like his last girlfriend, Sylvia, had always done.

As soon as he turned right onto Stink Dog Creek Road the woman told Hade to *continue seven point three miles, then turn right.* "Like there's any other way to get to Asheville from here," he muttered.

For the next 10 minutes the old Chevy cruised beneath stubborn rust-colored leaves that had not yet accepted it was November and fallen to the ground. Accompanied by the muffler's rumble and the driveshaft's chronic complaints about bad joints, Hade started singing John Denver's song about country roads. By the time he approached the intersection where he would turn onto State Route 1003, he'd completely forgotten about the GPS, so he was startled to hear the soft voice advise him, "In point five miles, turn right onto Hildie Anderson Memorial Highway."

Hade had never heard of *Hildie Anderson Memorial Highway.* He'd grown up in Fruition and knew the name Hildie Anderson from something important that went on in the county about the time he was in third grade. They'd even named a library for her over in the county seat, but he'd never known for sure who she was or what she'd done. It occurred to him that the woman in the box might know a few things he didn't, but he consoled himself knowing there were likely things he knew that she did not.

For a while then, it was smooth going between Hade and the GPS woman; none of her suggestions contradicted turns he already intended to make. The odometer clicked in time as Hade again sang the tune asking the country roads to take him home. He drove the routes he knew to drive, the woman offering dulcet affirmations at every turn. The two of them settled into what had all the appearances of a companionable relationship. Their interaction was so amiable Hade decided they should be on a first name basis. Problem was, he didn't know the woman's name.

The cardboard box she'd come in had *Garmin* written on it, but in spite of the exotic, foreign sound of it, *Garmin* just didn't seem to fit. Hade began running through the alphabet trying out a name or two beginning with each letter. When he couldn't come up with a single woman's name that didn't call up some bad experience he'd rather forget, he decided *Lady* was as familiar as he ought to be with the woman in the box. It was, after all, sort of a first date.

"You doin' okay over there, Lady?" he asked, trying on the name for size. When she had nothing to say, it occurred to Hade he might have found the perfect woman.

As the miles zipped by, one of the things that impressed Hade about Lady was her talent for estimating the time of his arrival at the freight center. On stretches where they ran into traffic and Hade had to slow down, the estimate inched a minute or two later. When traffic cleared and Hade was able to open the old truck up, the arrival time moved closer.

Just outside Asheville, Lady had them arriving at UPS at 12:17, over an hour before his 1:30 appointment. He'd only had a day-old sausage biscuit for breakfast and his stomach was already grumbling about the depravation. He knew by the time of the interview his belly could be the loudest voice in the room. There was plenty of time to swing into a Burger King and get a couple of Whoppers and a Dr. Pepper. An order of onion rings couldn't do any harm either. He knew there was a Burger King north of the mall on Tunnel Road. When he turned onto Highway 694 and Lady had nothing to say about it, he assumed she was in total agreement. Maybe she was getting hungry, too.

For a few minutes then, Lady was quiet. But when the truck wheeled off 694 onto Tunnel, and she brusquely informed Hade that she was *recalculating,* he thought he detected a hint of agitation in her voice. He didn't have to look her way to know she wasn't pleased with having to recalculate or that she blamed him for having to do it.

"Recalculating," she said again.

"Nothing to recalculate," Hade said, both eyes on the road but with an ear out for what, if anything, Lady might want to tell him when her recalculating was done.

Soon enough, she said, "In point two miles, turn right on College Street."

The Burger King was on Tunnel only a mile ahead. There was no reason to turn onto College. "Need to recalculate your recalculation," he said.

The truck sped past College Street. Lady again announced she was *recalculating.*

Hade triumphantly slapped the steering wheel. "Just like I said you should. Now who's telling who what to do?"

"In point four miles, turn right on Vance Gap Road."

The Burger King was now in sight. Hade had no intention of turning anywhere other than into the parking lot. He zoomed past Vance Gap.

Lady recalculated yet again, and in a voice Hade thought more a command than a suggestion said, "Turn right on Old Chunns Cove Road." Giving the woman no more deference than he would a wild turkey begging to not be shot, Hade passed Old Chunns and whipped into the Burger King.

"Recalculating," Lady said.

Hade picked up the little box and held it close to his mouth. He had a point to make and wanted to make sure Lady heard what he had to say. "Bullet in the bull's eye, possum up the tree. Right damn here where I wanted to be."

Lady, having apparently regained her composure and not the least bit bothered by repeating herself, let Hade know she was once again *recalculating*.

Thinking it might be best to shut Lady up before she asked for a cheeseburger or some fries for herself, Hade turned the GPS off and set it on the seat. "Stay put," he said, then got out of the truck and went inside.

A chubby girl with a constellation of acne on her cheeks and one silver ball a little bigger than double-ought buckshot poking out of the side of her right nostril took Hade's order. When she handed him the tray, he headed for the corner of the dining room where he hoped to enjoy a few minutes of peace and quiet; where there was no reason for anybody to recalculate anything.

The two Whoppers and super-sized onion rings, along with the large Dr. Pepper and a refill, turned out to be too much even for Hade. He got a to-go bag for the rings he couldn't finish. They would make a nice snack on the way home—celebration or consolation—there was never a bad time for onion rings.

Back in the truck, Hade tilted the rearview mirror to confirm he wasn't wearing part of his lunch on his face, or even worse, his new white shirt. He'd had no trouble finding the Burger King, but getting from there to the UPS Freight Center would require some help. He reached over and turned on the GPS. The little box blinked to life.

"Sorry if I said some things that hurt your feelings. I get grumpy when I'm hungry. What say we give it another go?"

"Recalculating," came the reply.

"That's my girl."

Hade stepped on the gas and pulled out onto Tunnel.

"Turn right on Tunnel Road."

"Already done it," Hade said. "Try to keep up. You want to ride with the big hoss you gotta stay in the saddle."

Ignoring the saddle remark, Lady said, "In point four miles, turn right on The Tully Spurlock Connecticut."

"The what?" Hade asked.

Lady hesitated for a long moment, then said, "In point three miles, turn right on The Tully Spurlock Connecticut."

Hade spied a sign ahead, TULLY SPURLOCK CONN. RIGHT LANE ONLY. "I think you mean *connector*, not *Connecticut*."

"In point two miles, turn right on The Tully Spurlock Connecticut," Lady insisted.

Hade turned right at Tully Spurlock without bringing up the *Connecticut/Connector* issue again. He was beginning to realize Lady might not be as smart as either of them thought she was. Truth was, he felt a little sorry for her. Asheville might not be his town, but at least he was from western North Carolina. According to a sticker on Lady's backside, she'd come all the way from Taiwan.

"Continue one point three miles, then turn right on Williamson Street Southeast," Lady said.

Straight ahead Hade could see a barricade stretching the entire width of Tully Spurlock. A DETOUR sign directed him to make a left turn. "What now, darlin'?"

At first, Lady didn't respond, apparently thinking things over before advising Hade to "Continue one point two miles, then turn right on Williamson Street Southeast."

"You can continue one point two miles if you got your heart set on it," Hade said. "But rather than bust through those saw horses, I think I'll follow the detour." He turned left.

"Recalculating," Lady said.

For the next half mile Lady repeatedly let Hade know she was *recalculating*. He couldn't be sure, but each time she spoke, he thought he detected a growing anxiety in her voice. "Okay. Try to relax," he said in what he intended to be a reassuring tone. "Take a few deep breaths. We've got this. You and me. We're a team."

He lifted the GPS onto the dashboard. "There. How's that? View's a lot better up here, isn't it? I'm going to head back toward the Interstate. You seem to be happier when we're near a big road."

"Recalculating," Lady assured him.

"You do that," Hade said.

A minute later he saw the elevated lanes of I-240 looming ahead. He pointed. "See. There's the Interstate. What's your best guess?"

"In point five miles, turn left on Addersville Avenue."

"Addersville?" Hade questioned. He'd never heard of Addersville Avenue, but there were lots of streets in Asheville he'd never heard of. That's the main reason he'd brought Lady along for the ride.

"In point four miles, turn left on Addersville Avenue."

"Whatever you say, sweetheart," Hade confirmed.

He moved the old truck into the left lane. A sign hanging above the intersection read ADAIRSVILLE AVENUE. "Maybe on the way home we can work on your pronunciation," he said as he made the turn.

"In point three miles, turn right on Anderson Drive," was Lady's reply.

Heading south on I-240 seemed like his best bet, but in spite of the *recalculating* nonsense and the construction snafu on Tully Spurlock, which really wasn't Lady's fault, so far she hadn't steered him wrong. Besides, he knew if he didn't do exactly what she told him to do, he wouldn't be able to blame her if he got lost.

"In point one miles..."

"I know," Hade said. "Turn right on Anderson Drive."

Hade flipped his turn signal, spun the wheel to the right, accelerated, and ran head-on into a white Lexus SUV stopped on Anderson waiting for the light to change. The impact sent the GPS caroming off the windshield, spraying a shower of black plastic and tiny metal shards around the truck's cab.

A diminutive, middle-age woman in a chartreuse pants suit exploded from the driver's side of the SUV, a cell phone clutched to her ear. Since the two vehicles were touching noses, blocking a direct route between the drivers, the woman raced around behind Hade's truck and stormed toward the window he was cranking down. Hade expected the conversation to begin with an inquiry as to his well-being, but he was met instead with a banshee scream and whirlwind of fury. *Hunnert pounds of lime green hell*, he would later tell Dixie Hooper.

Hade had a difficult time understanding much of what the woman was screeching at him, the words coming fast and furious and with a hint of a *Yankee* accent. But there was no mistaking the comments about his parentage and the woman's strongly held opinion that hillbillies like him should stay in the mountains on their one-lane dirt roads, tend to their stills, and stop being a menace to the civilized world. Perhaps most relevant among the woman's rantings was the lingering question: *Why the hell did you turn the wrong way down a one-way street?*

Hade would have liked to blame Lady, who after all had instructed him to make the turn, but after seeing her parts strewn about the truck cab like so much mechanical confetti, he decided to follow his raising and not speak ill of the dearly departed.

Both vehicles were drivable, so when the woman had finished her tirade, she backed her car onto the sidewalk. Trying to keep as much distance between them as he could, Hade pulled his truck off the road on the opposite side.

The unwinding of the mishap took a long time, including a lengthy discussion between two police officers over whether or not it was the Asheville City Police or the Buncombe County Sheriff's Office who should write up the incident, or whether they stood any chance of pawning the whole thing off on the North Carolina State Patrol. It was, after all, getting late on a Friday afternoon.

Long after the hour for Hade's interview had come and gone, the Buncombe County officer, who finally agreed to take jurisdiction, bid farewell with what Hade took to be a casual observation of practiced compassion: "At least nobody was seriously hurt."

The Lexus driver had a less compassionate final word for Hade, shaking her finger menacingly in his face and warning, "If your insurance turns out to be some of that bogus bullshit lizards and cavemen are selling, I'm coming after your ass, and believe me, I know where to come and how to get it."

Duly warned, and clutching a freshly written moving violation ticket he knew would be expensive, Hade climbed into the truck. He found the Burger King sack wedged between the seat and the passenger door. He took an unsatisfying bite of one of the remaining onion rings and dumped the others onto the floorboard. He gathered up as many fragments of Lady as he could find and dropped them into the bag. They hadn't really been that close, but it seemed like the decent thing to do.

On the long, lonely drive home, Hade had to admit he missed the soft, reassuring voice reminding him she was on the job—recalculating—when *recalculating* was exactly what needed to be done. He decided as soon as he could lay his hands on some cash he'd buy Dixie a new GPS. If he could lay his hands on enough, he might even get one for himself.

Richard Perreault lives on a mountaintop in western North Carolina overlooking the Great Smokey Mountains National Park. Up there in the rare air, he says, he receives massive amounts of support, inspiration, and tolerance from his wife, Sue, and cairn terrier, Darci Gayle.

PARENTS,

FOR BETTER OR WORSE

Moon of the Popping Trees

Hugh Gardner

First Prize

JUST BEFORE LAST NEW YEARS EVE, I FOUND MYSELF wandering in a frozen forest, utterly silent except for the light clatter of icy sleet hitting the tree limbs, and occasional faint snapping sounds. There was a full moon, very big and disorienting. Despite all my outdoors experience, I embarrassed myself by getting lost, until a neighbor pointed me back in the right direction.

Back in the warm home of our hostess, and the warm embrace of some old friends from the 70s she had gathered together, something floated up from my years of reading about Indian cultures which seemed somehow to fit the moment. The phrase that came to mind was "moon of the popping trees," so I asked someone to google it.

Moon of the Popping Trees, in the lunar calendar of the Lakota Sioux, was the most bitterly cold time of year, so cold that tree limbs would sometimes split and their frozen buds explode. It was during this moon 128 years before that a reconstituted and vengeful 7th Calvary, with 500 troops and four deadly Hotchkiss cannons, surrounded a peaceful encampment at Wounded Knee Creek in South Dakota and slaughtered 300 Lakotas, mostly old men, women and children. Twenty-four Medals of Honor were handed out to the soldiers who won this great victory in what came to be known as the last of the Indian Wars.

For the Sioux, this was the penultimate fracturing of their families and tribal clans, and thus their ability to resist the *Merrycats,* as they called Americans. But the coup de grace came only gradually over the next 75 years, as the Lakotas were robbed of their patrimony, their land and resources, and still worse, their culture. Their children were sent off to faraway, militaristic boarding schools where their tribal dress, their religion, even their language, was forbidden. Pop, pop, pop.

I was mulling this over that night, mesmerized by the star shower decorations our hosts had installed, dancing in the trees with millions of tiny, moving dots of green and red. Then it struck me how much our own communities and families had been similarly fractured into millions of random, swirling points of light. Unlike the Sioux, however, we Merrycats pretty much did it to ourselves.

My own family story is a pretty good case in point. Most Americans know nothing about their ancestors beyond their grandparents, if that, and I'm no exception. I know little of my paternal grandfather, except that his clan went west in covered wagons from Virginia for the 1889 Oklahoma land rush—and failed.

I come from *go-backers,* like most aspiring pioneers actually were, but they tried again in the 1893 sequel for more free lands taken from the Indians, and this time they stuck. Grandpa was a refrigeration engineer who built the first icehouse in western Oklahoma, a godsend in that dry and tortured land. He died young in a car wreck (I never knew him). During the Great Depression of the 1930s, my dad roamed all over the West following seasonal work, joining the CCC and sending money home, eventually working his way to a civil engineering degree and a career with the Corps of Engineers. By the 1950s, what was left of the family had scattered to the four winds, gone from Oklahoma forever. Pop.

My maternal grandfather didn't much like to talk about his past, but from what I gathered, he and his siblings were strongly motivated to leave an oppressive German family situation in Indiana. Westward expansion of the railroads—what today we call mobility, gave him a way out and he never looked back. He found an Irish girl in Chicago and moved to the Newton hub near Wichita, where he became the longest-tenured conductor on the Santa Fe. When I rode those thrilling rails with him as a child, I learned to cuss from his buddies in the caboose.

Grandpa also used his free railroad pass to visit old frontier towns in the Rockies where there were still whorehouses, long since banished in Kansas. After grandma died, he cut quite a rug with the old ladies in his white bucks, blue carnations, and seersucker suits. I visited him shortly before he died from a grapefruit tumor in his gut. His said he loved life and would keep after it until it was no longer worth getting out of bed in the morning. Pop.

His daughter, my mom, became a school teacher and administrator, and also died exactly when she wanted to, when my sister was visiting. His son, my only uncle, became a mortician. A couple of his kids still live in Kansas, beloved cousins and playmates as a boy, but long gone from me today. Pop, pop, pop.

I came along as a war baby who kept my dad home in Arkansas rather than fighting in WWII; his war, which he let me know he deeply regretted. My mom and I were the official reason for this stain on his manhood and honor. He was a dutiful father and good provider, but often beat me with his leather razor strap. He took me fishing, his sport, but would never come to mine, Little League baseball games. He got to drinking more and more as I grew up. Mom eventually threatened to leave him if he didn't quit, but not before I left home for good. Pop.

My dad was a paragon of Merrycat fatherhood in his time, a good man whose idea of love was discipline, whose hugs were red welts on my butt. I remember once asking him what a word meant, and he refused, insisting I go look it up in the dictionary. I wanted to hear it from him, my Pop (a term he always hated), but it must have worked. I learned my words well, the better to defy him.

When we ran head-on into the Vietnam War—I argued against it—he said just line 'em up and shoot 'em all. The breach between us grew to last for over 20 years. Thank God I was able to forgive and make peace with him in his last days. I think he secretly liked that I seemed to be such a bold and adventurous rake, like he was when young. Pop, dear pop.

He always pressured me to become an engineer like him, working for the government with a steady paycheck. Perhaps it was inevitable that I became a hippie intellectual instead. I know now that the beatings were not so much about me personally as his resentments from work, and the constraints imposed by parental responsibilities, and, I think, the loss of his peripatetic youth, when he had amazing adventures too and cut a pretty good rug himself among the girls.

Dad once told me he married my mom because she was the prettiest girl he could find before he went bald, one of few messages from him that I took to heart. My mom was widely considered an angel, but she had her dark side. She never once intervened in the beatings, though she might scold my father later. Once, in college in Austin, I made a C in one class and expressed an interest in coming back home for a while. "No," she responded, "I will not support a failure." She truly was mostly an angel, but the message was clear: You can't go home again. Merrycats are bred to leave and achieve. Pop.

After graduating college, more determined than ever to become autonomous, I had offers from several grad schools. I chose one as far away as possible. No matter which university I picked in the 1960s, the road not taken would have probably ended up in the same place. I felt it was my duty to go to the fateful 1968 Democratic Convention in Chicago to protest the war and get my fair share of abuse. Scholars estimate that some 20,000 cops and national guardsmen were deployed that day, outnumbering actual demonstrators by about 2-1. Like Wounded Knee, it was a slaughter.

In Grant Park, just across from the downtown Hilton, soldiers surrounded us on three sides with fixed bayonets and jeeps with barbed wire pushers while the cops attacked. I remember most of all the sickening stench of vomit, urine and fear, like Chicago's stockyards only a mile or two away. The Merrycats were killing their own children!

I escaped the worst by jumping 15 feet down into the subway corridor and catching the first train out. The bitter cold of this second great Civil War popped millions of buds both overseas and at home, breaking families and wrecking careers—a veritable star shower of pointless loss.

Thus I set off on a 40-year odyssey that took me from one coast to the other, from Alaska to Patagonia. I had surprising good luck and success in my early attempts at writing for publication, deluding me into thinking I could make a living as a freelancer. Some of the things I wrote changed history, at least a little, but they never impressed my parents, stern advocates of steady government paychecks like theirs. How else could I support a family?

My high-paying consulting gigs never seemed to turn into permanent jobs. I won several government talent shows but the political rule of three led to hires more likely than me to be a "team player." My outspoken history pegged me as a loose cannon. Gratifying but low-paying jobs in wildlife conservation, or writing fishing stories, didn't please my parents either. It became increasingly obvious that the root of their disappointment was my failure to deliver them grandchildren.

Lord knows I tried, at least promiscuously, but a few times with a whole heart (or as close as I could come to it). The three who wanted me most, I left behind; the three I wanted most left me. The particulars don't really matter. In my last and best attempt, I failed to make the transition from freelance adventurer to householder and good provider before she ran out of patience. She desperately wanted to have children, and I wasn't at all so sure. She made the right decision, and I came to feel I dodged a bullet, too, not taking the road to the toxic anger my father had, chafing at the obligations and restraints of marriage all the way. Pop.

Twenty years ago I spent the worst summer of my life at the hospital with mom every day for months. Among many terrifying moments, she cursed God for letting this happen to her. Miraculously, she survived, and once recovered, she paid off my sister's mortgage and my house in the foothills west of Denver, where I still live today, thanks in good part to the harsh discipline and frugality of my parents, which I finally came to appreciate.

My last serious girlfriend before I left the city, a former Japanese geisha, was furious: "You go up there you go crazy, you die lonely old man!" A fair prediction, but underestimating the power of place. As it turned out, I had a kind of rebirth in my quiet, semi-rural setting surrounded by mountains and wild critters of all descriptions, with a fine trout stream just down the hill. I have some good neighbors and some great friends for talking and adventuring. Best of all, I have two fine sons to make me proud, to go adventuring with, to look after my flabby old ass as I enter geezerhood. But wait a minute. How on earth could a three-time loser like me possibly have great kids?

In retrospect it does seem miraculous. It certainly wasn't planned, having long ago given up on mating and producing my own progeny. But subconsciously my lack of descendants ate at me, like acid in the heart, making a hole in me that wouldn't heal. It wasn't just that I was the last genomic unit in my father's family tree, the last to carry his name. It was more like a creeping feeling of meaningless. When I croaked, all the best of me, and him, would be forgotten; our brilliant points of light would wink out in the random swirl of insignificance.

The first time I met my two sons, they were the twin babies of one of my best friends from the 70s, a pioneering civil rights attorney who dropped dead of a massive coronary at 38 from the stress of trying to raise a family while pursuing justice for people who couldn't pay. I went to visit his widow now and then, and his two little hellions tearing up the place. When they were teenagers, we had a couple of bonding encounters at a ski resort and on a basketball court. But they increasingly got in trouble with the law, and in desperation, with no help from her own family or her husband's, their increasingly disabled mother turned to me to intervene. Under the threat of calling the cops myself, we cleaned out the stolen property they were fencing, and I took a more active interest. One joined the military, the other I helped stay out jail and get into college.

Over the years I made a point to keep in touch, helping out now and then with career counseling or fixing jams. One became an elite Marine officer, the other a successful businessman. They are both happily married and one has two daughters. At first it was just a vague gnawing in the gut, then I became a kind of protective uncle figure, then mentor, boon companion, and now, it seems, a godfather.

Today we talk all the time and take annual fishing trips together to keep our family spirit of adventure refreshed. On one such trip, the guide asked one of the boys if I was their dad. "No," said, "just a good friend of the family. He's like a father, only better." I like to joke that I got them at the age of reason, without the hassles of raising them. I feel blessed that I finally have two such strong roots under me. My property is deeded to them and they help pay my mortgage. They're my sons now.

I don't know what the secret of this odd parenting pattern is, but I would like to think it's some kind of unconditional love. That doesn't necessarily mean suspension of judgment. I opposed the one twin joining the military, but at least helped steer him away from kicking down doors. I was critical of some businesses the other got into, but never let him feel rejected. I guess the key is never losing interest or not expressing support, no matter how much you disapprove. You have to go where they are and let them know you've got their back.

What's left of my own original nuclear family is in a sad state. My sister had one son, the only grandson, who loved my parents (Memommie and Pal) and became everything I wasn't. He met a beautiful girl who motivated him to finally finish college, get a steady job as a teacher, and have four cool "great-grands," as my mom called them. My sister's no angel, but today, for reasons I can't fully fathom, she's banned from her son's house by her daughter-in-law, a tragedy shockingly common in Merrycat society; two of her grandkids have also fallen into this alienation. My nephew's heart is torn between these two stubborn, self-righteous women. No therapy (certainly not mine) has been able to bring the hostility to an end. My sister is increasingly bitter about this dreadful situation. Pop, pop, pop.

Back in the day, I once wrote a short biography of the great American psychiatrist Eric Berne, author of *Games People Play*. His basic theory was that our adult lives become reenactments of the fairy tales, myths, and parental mistakes we absorbed as children. We are not so much in charge of our own destiny, as we would like to think, but more like player piano rolls of music written long ago, fooled by our egos into thinking we were playing the keys.

I can see now how much my own life was written in the scripts of my ancestors. I followed my dad and granddad, even if in rebellion, more than I ever knew. I came to realize I had grown up in true Merrycat fashion, thinking we're supposed to strive relentlessly for personal advancement, believe in false meritocracies and hypocritical religion, be fearful of intimacy and never openly express love, always embrace the flag no matter what evils it carries, and leave home at the first opportunity to escape dysfunctional families and seek a better life.

If it weren't for the good parts of our Merrycat culture, as expressed by my Depression-era parents who made their own way and saved their salaries, I wouldn't be where I am today, or even alive. But if not for the bad parts of our Calvinist, capitalist, militaristic Merrycat heritage, America might truly be great again, perhaps greater than ever. We have plenty of money to fix our roads, Medicare for All, make college free, on and on, but it becomes increasingly questionable if we can even keep our democracy.

Sometimes it seems to me that our winning WWII was a kind of curse, leading to an arrogant and reckless determination to police the world. Our triumphalism has betrayed us and become trumpism, allowing corrupt oligarchs and their paid minions to rule us. We seem insanely out of control in spoiling our own nest: the sea, air, blood, soil, and wildlife that nurtured us. Instead of making a more perfect union as the founders envisioned, we Merrycats are perhaps more like the Lakotas, facing our own moon of the popping trees.

Hugh Gardner is a semi-retired social scientist and former muckraking journalist, political consultant, avid conservationist, and fly fishing adventure writer. His pre-digital articles appeared in many magazines, including *Esquire, Harper's, The Nation, Mother Jones, Rolling Stone, Human Behavior,* and *Playboy.* His Ph.D. dissertation was published by St. Martin's Press as *The Children of Prosperity,* a study of counter-culture communes in the 1970s. Copies are still available today on Amazon. Over a hundred of his fishing stories were published in *The Rocky Mountain News, The Angling Report, Rocky Mountain Streamside*, and *Wild on the Fly.* He lives today in Idledale, Colorado, near his favorite trout stream.

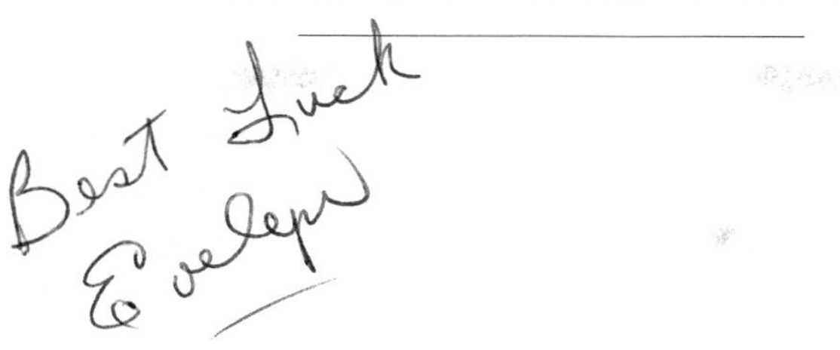

Mr. Joiner's Puppies

Evelyn Neil

Second Prize

FISTS CLENCHED AND ARMS PUMPING, WE RACED AHEAD of our parents the one block to Main Street. My long braids flapped across my back like windshield wipers. The wet ends of the sash on my favorite pink dress trailed along like the tails on a kite. Wearing my hand-me-down black cowboy boots, Jay struggled to keep up.

"Wait, Eslin," my little brother cried.

"Stop at the corner," our father called. "Don't cross the street."

We stopped as we were told and leaned against the warm red brick of the Ranger Hotel until Mother and Daddy caught up.

"Evelyn, turn around." Mother knelt behind me. "You got the ends of your sash in the toilet again."

"Sorry. I was in a hurry." I hung my head and stood very still.

"You need to slow down. Pay more attention." After jerking my sash tight around my waist and tying it into a neat bow, Mother spun Jay around, pulled up his denim pants and tucked in his cowboy shirt. "I'll be glad when he grows hips and can keep his pants up." She picked him up, slung him across her left hip and took off across the street.

"The hotel is four windows high." I held up four fingers. "Same as how old I am."

"That it is." Daddy held my hand in his big work-worn hand while

I skipped at his side across Third Street. "Find a place up front for you and your brother."

Jay in tow, I pushed through the crowd gathered on the sidewalk in front of the Midwest Hardware and found a place to sit on the concrete curb. Our parents settled in behind us and began to talk about cattle prices and the weather with friends and relatives. But soon, the conversation strayed to something else—the war.

"What do you think about this war FDR has gotten us into?" Daddy asked his cousin, Henry.

"Guess he didn't have much choice after the Japs bombed Pearl Harbor." Henry took off his Stetson, wiped his brow with a big white handkerchief and put his hat back on. "And it's about time we put a stop to Hitler running all over Europe." The rancher carefully folded his handkerchief and put it into the rear pocket of his black gabardine pants.

"Should be good for cattle and wheat prices," said Mother. "Troops will need to be fed."

"But will there be anyone left behind to help with lambing and calving in the spring or the fall harvest?" asked Daddy.

I stood and looked down the street. What is taking the parade so long? I wanted to ask if Daddy was going to go fight in the war, but knew better than to interrupt when adults were talking. Bud, who Daddy rode to work with, already went to the war. I hope Daddy doesn't go. He might get shot and never come home.

"How's your little Jean?" Mother asked Henry.

"Getting better. It was touch and go for awhile." He removed his hat and mopped his brow again. "She toddled out the back door and stepped smack in the middle of that rattler curled up sunning himself. Got her on the ankle."

"I'll bet your tires didn't touch the road once during that 30-mile drive to town," said Daddy.

"If it hadn't been for Doc Reckling, we would've lost her," said Henry.

I sat back on the curb with my elbows propped on my grubby skinned knees and cradled my chin in my hands. Jean is one year littler than me. She could've died. I'm glad we live in town where there aren't any snakes. Rattlesnakes are scarier than war. Will this parade ever start?

"You have such well-behaved children." My Sunday school teacher, Mrs. Crinklaw, suddenly appeared next to my parents and patted me on the head. "My, what a head of hair this child has. Are you taking them to the fair?"

"No, they're a bit young to sit through the rodeo, especially in this heat," Mother said. "This parade is a big enough challenge."

The distant beat of the bass drum followed by the strains of the Lusk High School fight song, *On Wisconsin,* brought me to my feet. I looked down the street to see a beautiful Palomino horse, just like Roy Roger's Trigger. Its rider, the Niobrara County Fair Queen, sat astride a polished brown saddle adorned with fancy flower designs and silver disks with long colorful ribbons. She wore a western-cut suit with embroidered red roses on the jacket. Her matching Stetson was the color of the horse's mane. The red, white and blue flag she carried rippled high over the horse's rump in the soft August prairie breeze. A few paces behind, a proud cowboy on a sleek black horse carried the red-bordered Wyoming flag with its blue field and white bison.

Daddy took off his brown felt hat and put his right hand on his tan khaki shirt below the Continental Oil Company name patch.

I grabbed Jay's arm. "Stand up."

"Why, Eslin?" He whined in protest and jerked his arm away. When he swung to hit me, I dodged.

"Put your hand on your heart like Daddy does when the flags go by."

After the flags passed, young men and some of the older men, too, began to hoot and whistle as the majorettes, dressed in beautiful white satin costumes decorated across the front with gold braid, strutted along twirling batons and swinging their short skirts. The high school band decked out in new red uniforms marched in straight rows close behind.

"Marj, Marj." I jumped up and down when I spotted my big sister. The mid-morning sun glinted off her gold sax as she marched past. She didn't look at me. Daddy put his hand on my shoulder.

Then came the cowboys and cowgirls of all ages and sizes riding black horses, brown horses and spotted horses. Some of the little kids rode Shetland ponies. The 4-H kids dressed in cowboy shirts and hats tugged and pulled goats, calves and lambs along the route. The tangy smell of sweaty horses and manure stung my nose. A fat clown in a white suit with big red dots danced along carrying a little shovel and bucket and picked up the poop. Another clown on the other side of the street had a bigger shovel and a barrel on wheels.

"Way to go, George," called a nearby man who smelled like he'd been to the Silver Dollar Bar.

I tugged Daddy's sleeve. "Is the clown's name really George?"

"Yes. He's the Midwest Hardware store man. He called your mother last week to say he was tired of sorting the nails and screws after you'd played in his revolving bins."

Hot and tired I sat back on the curb. Men dressed in black suits and tall black hats and ladies wearing colorful silk dresses and matching bonnets with ribbons and lace rode in black buggies with fringe on the top being pulled by prancing horses.

"Look, a car like Mr. Vollmer's." I pulled on Daddy's pant leg and pointed to an old black car chugging along. "Mr. Vollmer's driving it. The kids are in the back."

"It's Vollmer's Model A," my father mumbled more to himself than to me.

The floats, big trucks with the beds decorated in colored crepe paper and handmade paper flowers, carried men dressed in old-timey clothes and women in long print dresses and floppy sun bonnets. On one, children sat on straw bales and waved while the men and women danced to banjo music. I wish I could ride on a float again. Last year was so much fun riding on the float with Mother and the Sale Barn bowling team. I was their mascot and wore a red satin shirt with a long-horned steer painted on the back.

Excitement filled the air as the people along the street began to shout and clap at the next float. I stood to get a better look. On the truck bed was a huge meat grinder like the little one Mother clamped onto our kitchen table to grind left-over meat, onions and potatoes for hash. Mr. Joiner, the Piggly-Wiggly butcher, wearing a white apron with red stains on the front, stood next to the grinder and cranked the long handle. He lifted a brown and white spotted puppy from a big wicker basket and put it into the top of the grinder. Out the front came a long string of wieners. Men guffawed and roared with laughter. Women covered their mouths and shrieked. Children cried.

Mr. Joiner waved to the crowd and held a black curly puppy high over his head. The puppy squirmed and yelped, but the butcher laughed and dropped it into the grinder. He turned the handle and more wieners came out the front.

"Look, Daddy. Look." I pointed and cried in terror. "The puppies," I sobbed. I couldn't look. Everyone was laughing. I didn't see anything funny about puppies being made into wieners.

"Be quiet, Evelyn," hissed Mother, who was holding Jay asleep on her shoulder. "Don't make a scene."

"It's all right," Daddy said. "The puppies aren't being hurt."

I wasn't so sure. I tugged at Mother's skirt. I couldn't stop crying. Why was everyone laughing at Mr. Joiner and his puppies?

"If you can't behave like a lady, go home," said Mother.

I pushed my way through the smelly sweaty crowd and ran across Third Street without looking. I cried all the way home. Maybe Mrs. Riley will push me on the swing.

As soon as I entered the kitchen, the story of what I'd seen poured out in a stream of sobs and incomprehensible gibberish.

"It wasn't real. It was pretend," said our housekeeper.

"No, it was real. I saw it," I sobbed.

Mrs. Riley put a finger to her lips. "Hush, you'll wake your baby sister." She turned me around and gave me a little shove toward the door. "Can't you see I'm busy? Go outside and play."

I wiped my tears and runny nose on the hem of my dress. Will no one ever listen? Why does no one care enough to hold me on their lap when I'm sad?

I spied Sassafras lying in the sun near the front door. Maybe he cares. I hauled the big black cat onto the couch. His purring sounded like a stick being dragged back and forth across the washboard. When he began to knead his paws on my chest and suck on my dress collar, I clutched him close and told him about Mr. Joiner's puppies. He didn't care either. He just purred louder and sucked harder.

EVELYN NEIL grew up on the prairies of southeastern Wyoming where she acquired an early love for animals, wildflowers, western landscapes and expansive skies. She moved to New Mexico in 1957 and earned a BS from the University of New Mexico. She began writing in 2013 following retirement as president and CFO of the petroleum equipment company she founded in 1972 with her late husband, Don. She has been published in the *Anthology of the American Military Family, From the Frontlines to the Home Front.* Her work has appeared in *Southwest Sage* and the *Southwest Writers' Anthology.*

Evelyn lives in Albuquerque with her two cats and serves on the boards of the Albuquerque Guild of the Santa Fe Opera and of the Friends of the UNM College of Education.

A Proper Mother

MAUREEN KELLEN-TAYLOR

Third Prize

SHE SITS, BALLERINA-ERECT, IN A SMALL, ROCKING BOAT ON the dark waters of a channel edged by densely growing sugar-cane. Confidently cradling a light rifle, my mother surveys the water for signs of the alligator that attacked the women working immersed in the water.

My father, once a professional soldier, used to chuckle as he reported how she cleaned up the reptiles that his bullets missed. It is no mean feat to shoot an alligator in the eye from a rocking boat. Miss, and the bullets may ricochet off its hide and enrage the beast. Our family stories include past forays with frequent unpleasant surprises, like the time when, as their boat passed by, a large alligator launched itself off the high bank narrowly missing my horrified mother's lap by centimeters. These adventures did not deter my parents, who felt they had to protect the women who worked in these dangerous conditions to clear the fast growing weeds.

My mother was an interesting mix—adventurous, fun, gregarious, adaptable, strong-willed and, strangely enough, proper in that particular English way. Impeccable manners quietly spoken while expressing emotions loudly were unthinkable. I never heard her admit to being angry—irritated perhaps, disappointed, but never angry. She was too refined for such a gross emotion. There were often times when she was frightened, yes, being surrounded by a circle of large, poisonous spitting toads under a street light, or the sea of red eyes in the night water when our canoe was stranded on a river. Then she paddled the miles home as hard as the two men to get her child to safety.

How did this young woman, raised in a wealthy family in the heartland of England, leave her privileged upbringing for life on the edge of the wilderness in the humid South American tropics thousands of miles away from her family?

Love!...and war!

The war changed everything! Her life of ease with nannies, servants, birthday cruises in the Mediterranean, symphony and opera, social dances and ballerina-training disappeared. Air raids became a nightly occurrence as thousands of tons of bombs were dropped on her city. Survival became paramount as she witnessed her neighborhood and workplaces leveled, and friends and neighbors disappear without a trace. She was never confident that her home would still be there to return to at the end of each day.

On a fateful blacked-out train ride in 1940, she met a young soldier splendid in his red and navy dress uniform she later described. They spoke at length then, and through many letters afterwards, they fell in love. Seven weeks later they married, even though she was engaged to someone else. This urgency in wartime was not so unusual. My soldier father survived and, in the bleak aftermath of the war when many, many ex-military were looking for work, he took a job mechanizing sugar production in a remote colony in South America. For the very first time in their marriage, my mother went to live full-time with her husband, accompanied by their three-year-old daughter, on a sugar plantation compound in Demerara, British Guiana.

The English are famous for being stoic and this trait was honed by the privations of warfare and the scarcity that continued long after peace was declared. My mother's stoicism was essential as she found herself adjusting to a strange, wild land with enormous snakes and poisonous insects inhabiting the garden, and alligators and piranha in nearby rivers. Clouds of mosquitoes were constant companions.

The houses were equipped with kerosene lanterns because the electricity often failed. Household supplies came infrequently by ships from Canada and Britain. Instead of the theaters, galleries and grand hotels to which she was accustomed, there was one radio station and a 45-minute drive along a narrow dusty, pot-holed road to one of the capital's three cinemas. There was one dentist for the whole country and a rarely sober doctor to treat the white families' ills.

She seemed to adapt to all of these without much complaint and she came to love the country and the Guyanese people. But the social mores, prejudices and customs of traditional plantation life bewildered my mother and marked her as different, as much in her own mind as those of the planters. She couldn't bear the indolent, so-called superior life of the other wives on the whites-only compound, nor their gossip. She had to do something constructive, so she busied herself breathing life into the Governor's Committee for the Blind. She believed very strongly that with privilege comes responsibility and lived her life that way.

Her self-imposed mission was to locate adults and children who were injured and get them to medical care in the capital's hospital. Amidst the scandalized reaction of her fellow committee members and the compound neighbors, she intrepidly ventured into impoverished little villages where she was confronted by untreated injuries from horrible accidents and dire living conditions.

Oh, and she couldn't drive, so my father assigned her a driver, Khan, who also acted as scout for injured people. In spite of the traditional belief that it was dangerous for white women and girls to leave the compound unescorted by a white male, she and Khan set off several days a week into the back country on their search. She didn't seem to care that she was not supposed to do this. Like a single-minded bloodhound, she followed up on reports of a child here, blinded by a pencil stuck in his eye, or an old man there, living in a pit with cardboard for a roof. Contradicting the doom-saying of the white planters, regular streams of grateful relatives lined up at our door on Sundays to thank her.

For all of these wonderful traits, which taught me to try to make life better for others in some way, there were also times when my mother was possessed by the Ice Queen. I dreaded them!

The Ice Queen spread frost all around her and she communicated only in the briefest, most formal way. When my mother was upset with you, you were consigned to what my father humorously referred to as The Dog House. This could last for days or longer and was torture for me because, like my father, I tended to blow up when angry and then move on to a better state of mind. I remember, as a teenager, after spending a week or more in the dog house at the behest of the Ice Queen, I reached my limit. Out of deep frustration, I held my mother firmly by her shoulders so she had to face me and implored, "Talk to me! For God's sake, TALK to me!" But little changed!

There is a saying in the field of aging that you become more of who you are. This is often accompanied by the common belief that you can't teach old dogs new tricks (which has been contradicted countless times). However, it is very different to learn a new skill and much easier than unraveling and reworking a lifetime habit of coping behavior.

Many years later, I visited my mother, widowed and crippled with arthritis, who now lived in a small town in England. As my inherited sense of adventure had taken me to live in California, I only managed a few visits every year to her, each for about a week's duration.

On one of these visits, I realized I had upset her and, with sinking feelings, resigned myself to spending the last precious days of my visit with the Ice Queen. Mother was in her mid-eighties by then and I had no hope of anything changing, so I prepared myself for a disappointing and frigid end to my visit. As I observed her carefully (as only children are wont to do) I saw her struggle with her habitual response and with the reality that we only had a short time left together. Sadly, I had no bets on which would win. I knew of old that the Ice Queen would triumph and begin her long reign.

After only a few hours, I was amazed to see the frost visibly melt as she put whatever was bothering her on one side. In those short few hours, my funny, gregarious, adaptable, strong-willed mother emerged victorious, and we were off to enjoy being together one more precious time.

I have never forgotten that and, as I move into my own aging, I remember her breakthrough and have made it my own. I *can* continue to grow and change. I *can* wrestle with my own ways of coping that don't work anymore, and I *can* learn new behaviors. It is not easy, and when tempted to give up in that difficult struggle with old habits of mind and reactions, a little inner voice challenges me.

"If Mother could do it at 85, then you can!"

This story attempts to understand a complex relationship that spans generations and cultures. I developed a great deal of empathy for my mother during the process of writing about her, as well as surfacing a few important lessons for myself. Writing allowed me to put myself in her shoes as she navigated her way through a life that she had not been prepared for—neither the equatorial geography nor the cultural mores and values of plantation life. I now appreciate the scale of her adjustment—when to hold fast, when to compromise and when to embrace.

Maureen Keller-Taylor grew up, an emotional West Indian raised by progressive English parents, living in a segregated compound on a sugar plantation, bordering the Bush (the wilderness) in Guyana. Each day was an immigration from the racist plantation environment to a multiracial school and social life in town.

Later, moving heartbroken from a country she knew and loved, to England, she hid her loneliness in studying art. She left England a few years later to fly with PanAm and unprepared, to live in New York City. After traveling to Asia, the Middle East and Europe in the 60s, she settled in San Francisco, learned to be a wife and mother and later found her career path in Socially Engaged Arts. All through her life she has been marked by her childhood in the borderlands with the wild. This led to various trainings and groups concerned with extreme weather and ecology.

On reflection, she has been instrumental, sometimes unconsciously, in helping people of all ages to connect with their creativity, at the cost of her own creative expression. Currently in Southern California she continues to encourage using the arts to affirm identity and to pass on legacy to younger people in intergenerational projects, most recently, with a university team of graduate students collecting videoed stories from older adults.

Consequently, she enthusiastically promotes Ageless Authors to older storytellers. This year, staring retirement in the face and questioning her habitual stance of "I'm not a writer," she entered the Ageless Authors Writing Contest for the first time. Since Ageless Authors accepted her story, and with new found courage, she has told another Guyanese story in front of a live audience. This is her farewell to California before moving to Fort Worth, Texas, for more adventures.

The Broken Watch

TANK GUNNER

Honorable Mention

WEBSTER WATSON WAS NINE WHEN HE LEARNED A lesson in truth and responsibility. He had intended to secure and protect the valuable timepiece entrusted to him by his older friend. But when things turned sour, Webster found himself in a perplexing predicament.

Web—he never liked the name Webster—happened to be standing in the end zone for Friday night football when the school bus arrived. As varsity players strode past, each called his name or gave a playful punch on his arm. He was popular with kids of all ages in Palomino.

Web's popularity existed because his Dad owned the appliance store in town. In the store, of course, were Tappan gas stoves, Amana refrigerators, Oster Osterizers, Sunbeam Mixmasters, Hoover vacuum cleaners with a small headlight, and Philco and Motorola radios. The newest item was the Motorola television set framed in a faux mahogany cabinet. This magnificent piece of fake furniture even had double doors that opened to expose the bulging TV screen. Shows were in black and white. Programs in living color were not yet a reality.

Webster's Dad received two of five delivered in Lamar County. McClarren's Appliances in Paris received the other three.

One was on display in the front window of Watson's Appliances. The other sat in Web's living room. People would stand on the sidewalk outside Mr. Watson's store and watch the test pattern. It was mesmerizing.

Three nights each week, Mr. Watson left the TV on so people in Palomino could watch Milton Berle's Tuesday *Texaco Star Theater* and Pabst Blue Ribbon Beer's *Friday Night Fights.* Saturday evenings, cars double-parked on Main Street while townsfolk stood seven deep to enjoy Lucky Strike's *The Hit Parade.* It was great entertainment.

Schoolmates were nice to Webster because they sought an invitation to come over and watch the soundless test pattern broadcast by the Texarkana television station 30 minutes before Buffalo Bob and Howdy Doody.

Mark Kitchens, the Palomino High School star punter, tight end, and defensive linebacker stopped in front of Web. Mark slipped off his Timex with the elastic metal band and shoved it toward Web.

"Hold your arm out, Web." Mark slid the watch onto Web's left wrist. "I forgot to leave my watch in the locker room. Can I trust you with it?"

"Sure, Mark. Boy, that's a nice watch."

"It's a Timex. Wear it. Take care of it for me. I'll get it after the game."

Now, the mystery became whether the wristwatch was already broken when Mark passed it to Web, or Web broke it while horsing around, by winding the stem too tight, or banging it on the ground. Perry Mason and a courtroom jury could only decide the outcome of this dilemma.

This fact was indisputable: after playing catch and tackle in the end zone with other friends during halftime intermission, Web discovered the damn thing was broke.

He stayed until the two-minute warning at the end of the game, then he got the hell out of Dodge. He did not want to face Mark to return his watch, which was no longer ticking—in spite of what Mr. John Cameron Swayze proclaimed.

At recess on Monday, Web was pinned.

"Gimme my watch," Mark demanded. The tenth grader towered over the third grader.

"I don't have it."

"Where is it?"

"At home. I forgot to bring it."

"Why didn't you wait for me at the bus to give it to me after the game?"

"My mom called me. I had to go home."

When a Mom called in Palomino, kids responded—even if it wasn't their mom. Mark knew the consequences of ignoring a yelling mom, so Web's excuse appeased him.

"Well, you better bring it tomorrow, or I'll punch your face in."

Web was in trouble, big trouble. Mark was a man of his word. Web knew a punch in the face would hurt like hell. Bashed-in face, broken nose, blinded, front teeth knocked out? It was time now to do it if Web had known how to shudder.

What to do? Web couldn't say it was lost—could he? No, that meant he would have to buy a new one, with money he didn't have.

Next day at first recess, Mark found Web hiding behind the huge world map ball that sat in a wooden frame in Ms. Pruitt's classroom.

"I been looking for you, Skunk. Where's my watch?"

"Oh, I forgot. I was late this morning and ran out of my house without it."

"This is the last time. If you don't have it tomorrow, I will break your arm. You hear me?"

How could Web not hear? Mark's voice was loud enough to alert Palomino's Town Constable, Twig Chestnut, that trouble was afoot.

When Mr. Watson came home at the end of the day, he asked Web about Mark's watch.

"Mr. Kitchens came by the store this afternoon asking about Mark's watch. He said Mark asked you to hold it for him at the ball game Friday night, and now Mark can't get it back. Do you have the watch?"

Busted. "Yessir."

"Bring it to me."

Web pulled the broken watch from under his pillow and relinquished it to his Dad.

"Why didn't you give it back?"

"It's broke. I was afraid to tell Mark 'cause he would punch my face in."

Mr. Watson smiled. He understood the situation.

"How do you know it's broken?"

"It don't run no more. It stopped ticking."

"Did you break it?"

"I don't know. Maybe."

"How so?"

"I might have wound it too tight, I think. The stem don't move no more."

"I see. Well, I'll bring it down to the jewelry store in the morning and let Mr. Jeffries have a look at it.

"Now, Web," Mr. Watson placed a comforting hand on his son's shoulder, "Mark trusted you with his watch, and you violated that trust. It was your responsibility to take care of it, and you didn't. When a person gives you their trust, you must do everything in your power to protect that trust. And, you lied to Mark instead of telling him the truth."

"If I'da told him he would've bashed in my face, knocked my teeth out, broke my nose. I coulda been blinded for the rest of my life."

"I understand that, Son. But Mark would have respected you if you had told him you broke his watch and would pay for its repair. Truth, trust, and responsibility are more important than a broken timepiece. Can you understand that?"

It took two days for Mr. Jefferies to fix the watch.

Mr. Watson paid $1.95 for the repair and cleaning.

The lesson Web learned was worth more than a cheap-ass Timex.

Mark stewed for two days and gave Web the evil eye every time they passed in the hallway at school, but he did not break Web's face.

When invited to watch the black and white test pattern on the Motorola, Mark forgave Web.

But Mark wasn't sure he could trust Web again.

Tank Gunner is the pen name of a retired combat cavalry trooper, senior parachutist, and jumpmaster. He has been awarded a Combat Infantry Badge and decorated with a Silver Star, a Purple Heart, and three Bronze Stars, one for valor. He served his nation with pride and honor for more than a quarter century as an enlisted soldier and officer. Tank's third book, *Cookie Johnson,* follows his contributions to the anthologies *Prompts* and *Prompts Too,* which are filled with entertaining and engaging short stories written in his superb style. He and his wife live near Dallas with Toby.

Plaques

ROBERT NELIS

Honorable Mention

WHEN HE CALLED HIS OLDEST DAUGHTER, MARY, TO ASK assistance in moving out of the family homestead, she said she'd be happy to help.

"But dad, I won't touch mother's plaques." After a short hesitation she added, "You deal with them."

"Neither your brother or sister wanted to handle the plaques either."

"Dad, you know exactly why."

"Okay. I will box up the plaques."

Mary again hesitated before answering. "Whatever, Dad."

After the call, Jim sat back in the soft living room chair and reflected on the 30-some plaques hung on the walls. The house was too large for one person and it now only functioned as showcase for these testimonials.

Jim walked to the kitchen, poured a coffee, and sat at the table. Smiling, he remembered how Carol was actually a great mom when the three children were small. She dressed them well, fed them healthy food, and undertook school parental activities.

The change started when six-year-old Mary became a scout. Carol volunteered to lead the troop when the existing one resigned for personal reasons.

The troop had been floundering as evidenced by the shrinking number of girls and declining number of project activities. Carol's enthusiasm and energy seeped into the operation. By launching a dynamic camping program and undertaking interesting handicraft projects, parental interest increased; the number of scouts doubled.

After recognizing the successful revitalization, the regional scouting leaders awarded Carol her first plaque and offered a regional position. Every year the regional organization awarded plaques to its officers, so Carol gathered numerous ones as she rose up the ranks.

With a slight smile but while shaking his head in the negative, he continued to remember Carol's organizing skills. The district officers observed Carol's successful term as regional president and offered a district position. Its time commitment precluded involvement in the local troop so she resigned and received a plaque.

After hearing of her mother's resignation, Mary said to him, "This is great, I don't have to be the perfect scout, daughter of the perfect leader." In fact, for her, scouting lost its shine compared to playing soccer.

Carol's new duties required working at least four nights a week and sometimes one weekend day. It only required two years for her to reach the second vice president position. Her most noted achievement, that earned a plaque, concerned the development of a highly regarded training seminar on initial troop organizing. After presenting the seminar at the state convention, some national scouting professionals took notice.

Returning to the living room, Jim stood in front of the plaques display and sipped the cooling coffee. As a wedding present, his parents gave them an original oil painting of a sailing ship sea battle. They hung it on the living room wall and, as time went by, he surrounded the painting with an accumulation of family photos. One day the ship painting had sailed to the hall wall next to the bathroom door; the photos traveled with it. Plaques filled the wall space. Carol became quite skilled at hanging and relocating numerous different sized and shaped commendations.

The national scouting professionals offered her a position for which living and transportation expenses were paid. The position required extensive travel but Carol jumped at the chance.

Jim said out loud while putting the cup on the table, "God damn it. The national position became an addiction. Power and excitement, shit." He flopped into the chair.

Each new national level task Carol completed won her another plaque. The scouting world considered several of the beautiful bronze awards to be quite an honor.

Carol reached the national president's office. By this time the family only saw her on weekends. She would fly home on Friday nights and depart on Sunday evenings.

These memories proved a little unsettling. Jim decided to wander into his kid's bedrooms and look at the walls. The kids wanted to match their mother's successes so they became almost fastidious about hanging up numerous academic and athletic awards. Sophie even pinned up high school report cards.

Carol witnessed none of these achievements. Jim attended all games and award ceremonies; all parent/teacher conferences; and celebrated any of the kid's successes with pizzas.

The closet across the hall from the bathroom contained the cleaning equipment. Jim stopped and looked in. Carol made two efforts to show her love. First, she cleaned like a maniac on Saturday from top to bottom using the vacuum, dust rags, and strap on a tool belt containing various cleaning supplies. Family members learned never to leave anything important out; all unsecured items went into the trash.

Second, all birthday parties occurred as a celebratory brunch on Sunday. She would rise at 5 A.M. to prepare the event's food taken from the *Quick and Good* cookbook, and bake the cake.

Jim entered the dining room which contained a sharp memory. Several years ago, while Carol pursued her national responsibilities, the kids and he sat at their usual family Sunday dinner. His son asked, "Dad, does mom love us?" He tried to hide his own feelings while explaining that Carol loved them very much.

"Come on dad," Mary said, "Mom resented how we dumped scouting in favor of sports. She never forgave us. Do you remember when the West High Lady Knights played in the state semifinal soccer game?"

"Your dumb Knights lost." George said. Sophie snickered.

"Shut up you two," Mary flipped a middle finger at them. "Your teams never got that far." They all laughed.

She faced Jim. "Mom deliberately arranged a schedule conflict so she wouldn't have to come. She never came to any." Both siblings shook their heads in the affirmative.

Mary then stood up, walked over to where Jim sat, and kissed him on the cheek. "Dad, I'll always remember kicking a goal in that game because you out-shouted all the other fans."

He had tried several times to explain to the kids that their mother really loved them. The fixation on performing well just temporarily moved her position responsibilities above family matters. He knew none of them ever bought the logic.

He returned to the living room and sat down. Remembering one painful incident triggered another. On one of Carol's weekend visits during the third month working at the national, she lay in bed and with a big smile pulled down the sheet revealing a naked body. "Come on Jim, I don't wish to abandon my wifely duty."

He remembered standing almost frozen. "Carol, a once a month quickie only emphasizes you're vacating this marriage. I decline your invitation."

She slowly pulled up the sheet and said with unrestrained anger, "Look Jim, I perform an important service for tens of thousands of girls all over this country. I need to escape from the pressure of my responsibilities by periodically acting like a simple wife and mother."

"I can think of three kids and a husband who could use more than periodic consideration," he said, walked out of the room and with the exception of perfunctory public kisses never sexually touched her again.

Sunlight poured into the living room through a large picture window. Jim stood up, walked over to it, and without focusing stared out. The kids wondered what their relationship would be once Carol left the national presidency. The new president did not want the outgoing one to hang around.

Not wanting to lose Carol's talent, the professional staff offered her the paid presidency of the Illinois scouting organization. Without any family discussion, Carol just announced the new responsibilities.

Sophie's reaction to this new job reflected all of their feelings. "Tell mom, I'll send her a post card once a month."

Jim turned and looked at the plaques that by this time, with the addition of the national awards, spread to the room's sidewalls. The new plaques caused Carol to reject and box up the less prominent ones.

He revisited the kitchen, refilled his cup, and then sat at the table. Sophie's prediction proved to be correct. Before the cancer struck, Carol again threw herself into the state job. The job required extensive travel around the state—she put 30,000 miles on the car—which resulted in her only being home for shortened weekends. The flow of plaques continued.

Mary, George and Sophie planned to arrive at 10 A.M. A fresh pot of coffee was needed. He opened the pantry closet door and saw one of Carol's two wigs sitting on the shelf. It sparked another round of memory as he made the coffee.

The liver cancer caused a real struggle for Carol to keep up the work pace. However, chemotherapy's side effects made it impossible and forced a despised resignation. Considering her absolute fixation with the job, Jim never could tell which caused more personal grief, the malady or the resignation.

Scouting organizations all over the country sponsored farewell banquets for her. Of course, each stop produced another plaque or stand-alone crystal trophy.

Remembering the incredible strain placed on him and the kids to transport a disabled person around the country, he said out loud, "God damn that was hard."

Because the disease stopped the ability to hang plaques, she quietly asked Jim to put up the new ones. "It would mean a lot to me." The request stirred pity and he complied. Carol never heard his whispering to each one, "Fucking bastard," as it was hung.

At the end, Carol became bedridden. The whole family agreed her bed should be placed in the living room. They guessed Carol would find strength from the plaques.

After looking at his watch, Jim jerked to a standing position and said out loud, "Shit, the kids will be here in an hour. I've got to get going."

First, he took the rejected plaque box to the trash can because she herself had dismissed them. He divided the remaining plaques into three boxes with each child receiving a representative selection of beauty and prestige.

George arrived first with a cherry strudel coffee cake—Jim's favorite. "First the coffee cake," Mary said when she arrived, "then you assign us tasks."

"Okay, you guys, first thing you must get the junk off your bedroom walls."

"Come on dad, they are awards." Mary and Sophie smiled.

"Okay, awards," he said. "And while speaking of awards, ah . . . I've divided mom's best plaques into three boxes, one for each of you."

The group's sugar-enhanced good feeling instantly departed. The three sat stone-faced. After a few moments Sophie looked Jim in the eye, "Okay dad." They stood and began their assigned tasks.

Jim heard music playing as the work progressed. About noon no sound of the work existed. A quick search showed that the children were not in the house. He found all three in the backyard standing around a 55-gallon drum the neighbor used to burn scrap wood at construction sites. George had started a fire in it. They were each taking turns tossing plaques into the fire.

With some surprise in his voice, Jim said, "What the hell is going on?"

They all directed calm facial expressions at Jim then resumed pitching the plaques into the fire. When he took a step closer, Mary said, "Dad stay out of this. We'll handle mother's legacy in our own way."

Nodding his head in the affirmative, Jim turned and climbed the back stairs. He stood on the porch for a few moments and watched his children's testimonial. After entering the kitchen, he poured himself another cup of coffee and sat at the table holding the cup with both hands. Jim cracked a small smile.

Robert L Nelis began his writing career as he commuted to and from his job as a municipal official in Chicago suburbs, creating characters and laying out plots as he drove. Now retired, he enjoys having time to write the stories he planned over his 27 years of commuting. Rob received a master's degree in urban planning and policy from the University of Illinois, where he also served as adjunct faculty. He lives in Chicago with his wife of 42 years in a 110-year-old house and enjoys his four grandchildren.

Seven is the Magic Number

Kenneth Michael Stewart

Honorable Mention

I WAS A BUG BOY. I WOULD SPEND HOURS STUDYING BUGS and was very curious about social insects. Wasps are social insects. Cats, curiosity, lives. If I were a cat, I would have had seven lives. I would watch my wasps on their paper nests, tending their young. Even when they were quiet, they would continuously tap one foot gently on the paper, as if they had restless leg syndrome—or would it be restless foot syndrome?

The wasps built their nests under exposed boards in our chicken-less chicken coop on my mother's farm. I had to capture these nests. In the early spring, I would approach a nest, slowly and carefully, holding a glass Mason jar. The nest was small and there was only one wasp. Slipping the mouth of the jar over the nest, I would move the jar, breaking loose the nest which fell to the bottom of the jar. The wasp, also trapped, would soon settle on the fallen nest. After slipping the lid, with air holes previously punched, over the top of the jar, I would take my prize home.

As spring turned into summer, I captured more nests, each larger than the last. First two, then three, then four wasps. As I approached, each wasp would turn and follow me. Hugging the nest with four legs, it would point at me with the other two, the tip of one beating the air slowly, in its restless foot syndrome way.

Safely outside my Mason jars, I watched new wasps being born. I saw them dry their wings and gain the ability to fly. I captured a five-wasp nest. I captured a six-wasp nest. Then I tried for seven. Approaching slowly, seven sets of compound eyes followed me. Before I could cover the nest, one wasp took flight, stinging me on the forehead, right between my eyes. Instantly there was a knot, red and half the size of a golf ball. I ran home, screaming.

My mother was different, but I knew she would be there when I needed her. She held my head in her lap and gently applied wet baking soda to the sting to draw out the poison. She would use the same technique on another occasion when I crossed paths with a bumblebee. The home remedy worked and the pain gradually receded.

Maybe if I had continued, I could have captured an eight-wasp nest. Maybe if I had been lucky, I could have succeeded with nine wasps. Actually, I never captured another nest. I decided that seven is the magic number.

This bug boy learned other lessons. I had devoured numerous articles about wasps. Nowhere had I seen any mention of the restless foot syndrome. No expert ever mentioned that when I stared at wasps with curiosity, they stared back with fear and anger. I learned that wasps could think. I learned that experts could not.

What makes a bug boy? A scared wasp? A mother? That just mentioned bumblebee? Or, perhaps, polio? I remember little of that long ago September, but I think it played a part.

Pain is not something we remember well, but it does keep us from precisely noticing anything else. My temperature was high, 103 degrees or more. I vaguely remember bottles of glucose, suspended, with the clear liquid running down a tube, into my arm. I do know that I had an extreme headache, while at the same time the muscles in the back of my neck ached—however, the word "ached" means a dull pain and this pain was definitely not dull. My only escape was sleep.

They took me to the hospital. I had been there before, at a time when the slightest sore throat meant your tonsils had to come out. A doctor's gloved hand had pushed me against a cold, hard table. The light was blindingly bright, accenting his white coat and mask. I could not escape his other hand, which held something tied to a long hose. It was black and round and designed to cover my face. Fear, suffocation, blackness. Later, ice cream.

My mother had deserted me, but she came back. She always came back. Smiling, with ice cream for my sore throat.

My second trip to the hospital taught me that all doctors are white-coated monsters, to be avoided at all costs. They told me I had polio. I would have never had polio if they hadn't told me. Polio was like a very bad flu that lasted for three excruciating weeks. Then I had to deal with the aftermath.

My mother was different. She had a job, at Sears, as a buyer's assistant. She was gone all day, it was just me and my grandmother.

I must make my writing different. My goal is not to be just a famous author. I want you to know that I have unique thoughts. I want you to know my ideas are mine, and mine alone.

What is this essay about? What is its genre—fiction, nonfiction, creative writing, mystery, or some strange mixture? I think of it as primarily nonfiction, but speculative. I speculate who and what would I have been if I had never had polio. I speculate what made me who I am. These speculations are part of everything I write—maybe even everything I think.

When I felt better, they told me I was in Isolation Hospital, an aptly named place for mainly kids. These were the dangerous, the contagious. I had never been dangerous before. A lot would happen to me in the next few months, but the important thing was the pain was gone.

I was in an iron lung, a massive device I had only seen in photos. Its purpose was to help my breathing. I have no memory of breathing being a problem, just the swooshing sound of the strange contraption. The iron lung was primarily a metal tube, approximately six feet long and four feet in diameter. I don't remember how the lung was supported, but the tube part was horizontal and could be rolled around the room. It looked much like a one-man submarine with portholes on the side. One end was permanently covered with a heavy airtight rubber membrane.

A motor was attached that moved this membrane in and out in a breathing-like motion. The speed of the motor was set to exactly mimic human breathing. The other end of the tube was covered with a metal disk that resembled a trash can lid.

This lid was conditionally airtight. It had a hole in the center designed large enough to get my head through. On one side, the outside part of the lid, was a supporting pillow. Attached to the other side was a bed. This entire section of the iron lung (pillow, lid, bed) was on wheels. To close the lid, this section, with my head on the pillow, neck in the hole, and body on the bed, was rolled into the tube. A collar around my neck—it was tough and sponge-like—made the inside of the lung airtight. I understand now that as the air pressure inside the iron lung fell and rose, air flowed into and out of my lungs.

My mother was different. She was divorced. I only knew of one other person who was divorced and he was divorced from my mother and had died. The year I had polio, my mother stopped being divorced. She remarried and moved away—to the farm.

Perhaps I should tell you about The Slinky Incident. Fear (first, the flash, then fear of discovery) cemented the memory for me, but I have to use logic to fill in the details. It must have been just after Christmas, the Slinky, a metal spring-like toy that can walk down stairs, a likely present from my mother. She would have never given it to me if she had recognized the danger.

I had never been made to go to bed, but the routines of a hospital are different. The long hallway outside my room was dark and deserted except for a single nurse, vaguely visible, at her far away station. The whole wing was dimly lighted, but not pitch black. All the young patients were assumed to be sleeping.

I thought I had spunk. No one could tell me when to go to sleep. Looking back, the term spoiled brat seems accurate.

Spunky, spoiled, whatever, that night I was bored. The lamp by my bed was off, but plugged into a dual electrical outlet. The second outlet was empty. I wondered what would happen if I stuck my Slinky into this outlet?

I first had to pull the metal spiral apart and bend one end slightly—this end could then be inserted into the empty socket. I was stupid, but not that stupid. I used two sticks, two wooden spoons, two non-conducting somethings to maneuver the Slinky into fateful contact.

There was a blinding flash. A noise, shorter and not as loud as thunder. A burning smell. Total darkness. Far away shouting. Then flashlights and talking outside my door. After an eternity, the lights returned. Hiding under my covers, I dreaded discovery and condemnation. When it finally seemed my deed might go undetected, I fell asleep, safe.

I have kept my guilty secret for more than half a century. Now you know.

When I left the hospital, my right leg was weak. I was on crutches. I believe I could have walked without them, but I don't know. I don't remember.

I visited the physical therapist regularly and performed muscle strengthening routines religiously. No matter how much I tried, I could never do a pushup or a chin-up, my shoulders and arms were too weak. I saw great athletes do pushups and chin-ups using one arm, but I could never accomplish this. Perhaps I had lost some muscle.

When it was time for me to return to regular school, the question of whether I should enter the fifth grade or repeat the fourth grade came up (my two fourth grades together only totaled about half a year). I hated school, but somewhere I had gotten the idea that it was important, not from my mother, a daughter of a former coal miner. She was indifferent to the value of an education. I did not want to spend an extra year in school and my good grades made it my mother's choice. When I made my desires known, in my usual spoiled brat way, she let me decide.

Regular school included physical education (PE). For me, this was extremely embarrassing and dangerous. I passionately dreaded and feared PE. The only thing I feared more was not going to PE and being seen as different, me the kid who desired uniqueness and didn't care what people thought feared being noticed, being different.

I was the worst kid at things like the previously mentioned chin-ups and pull-ups, as well as the related rope climb. I was the slowest runner. Despite all this, there was an instance when I received public praise from a coach as someone who never gave up and always tried his hardest. Ironically, this praise was a source of extreme embarrassment and much misery.

Tumbling was dangerous and I knew it. I had to run across a pad, put both hands down, temporarily support my body, then duck my head and roll onto my back. My right arm was the problem. On each tumble, I must have looked like an airliner landing, where the landing gear collapses on touchdown. I don't know how I kept from breaking my neck.

This was a time when mothers, especially my mother, took no part in school activities. All decisions were mine and this seemed normal. You might think my mother didn't love me, but then how do you explain that, for the six months I was in the hospital, she arrived every day right after work and remained until the 9 P.M. curfew?

After I left the hospital, many things happened that made me miserable. Some things happened because people did not know I had polio. Other things happened because people did know.

At some point PE ended. At some point I stopped visiting the physical therapist. My crutches were gone. Physically, I was much closer to normal. Mentally, I was weird, but I took comfort in believing that we are all weird.

A childhood with polio and white-coated monsters should be a horrible, dreary place. That is not how I remember my childhood.

Shortly before the monster came the second time, my mother remarried. My mother and I had been living with my grandparents. I didn't like my stepfather. I don't believe it had anything to do with my mother. He just wasn't a very nice guy.

My stepfather and mother soon purchased a farm a few miles away. When asked if I wanted to live with her or my grandparents,

I instantly decided to stay with my grandparents. Both before and after my bout with polio, my evenings were full of things kids liked. I loved science and studied bugs and stars. With my friends, I played the sport of the season. My fondest memories were the weekends. Often with a visiting friend, with the farm at the center, I would explore the world.

I never thought of my mother as dumb. She was the smart one in the family. Something happened, however, when I was in my early teens, that made me wonder.

My mother, at a late age, had decided she wanted to drive. In preparation for her driving test, we decided to take the family sedan, a 1950 black, two-door Ford, for a spin. Seat belts were not part of this picture. We, in this case, were my mother driving, my grandfather riding shotgun, and me in the back seat.

Our departure from the farm and the drive itself were uneventful. Our return was not. My grandfather simply suggested that my mother turn into the driveway.

Our Ford took out the mailbox, somehow spanned a small ditch, and stopped in our front yard. My grandfather, I think in shock, asked my mother why she had not used the brakes, had not slowed down. My mother explained that she didn't know how to slow down. She had always thought that the brakes were only for stopping.

Mike Stewart was born in Memphis, Tennessee. He received a Bachelor of Science Degree from the University of Tennessee in mathematics and physics. After working for IBM in Huntsville, Alabama, Mike formed his own company in Memphis. His career spanned 40 years, moving from computer support to internet applications. After retirement, Mike wanted to write something different. One of his stories was designated a semi-finalist in the 2017 Woven Tale Press Literary Contest. He lives in Collierville, Tennessee, with his wife, Mary. They have a son and two grandchildren.

Exits and Entrances

HEDDA HERZOG

Honorable Mention

A REAL LIVE LETTER. NOT AN EMAIL, TEXT, TWEET, FACEbook post or even a telephone call. Instead, handwritten words wriggled their way across the plain white paper envelope. I didn't recognize the sender's name or address in the upper left-hand corner. But, when I looked closer, it said "Researcher, WPA artist H. Herzog," scribbled next to it. I knew *that* name, it was my father's.

In 1935, as part of his effort to combat the effects of the Great Depression, President Franklin Delano Roosevelt established the New Deal, a program to get America back on target. In what became the Works Progress Administration, the government paid millions of people to perform a variety of jobs. The WPA, as it was known, made a special effort to employ many artists, writers, musicians, and actors.

In that pre-TV, pre-digital era, posters promoted social programs such as health and safety as well as the benefits of activities like travel, sports and the arts. At a time of deep national despondency, they projected a positive image of the country and where it was hopefully heading in the future. Several cities and states created WPA poster divisions. The one in New York City flourished and attracted accomplished and highly respected artists.

Employed by this division, my father was lucky to have any kind of work at all during the depression, especially in his field. He created posters on a variety of topics. Among these was a depiction of Yosemite National Park, a promotion for New York City's municipal airports, an announcement for a play about Abraham Lincoln as well as one for a children's art exhibit. Many of his posters are now in the Library of Congress in Washington, D.C, and other public and private collections.

When I opened the envelope I read "Currently I am researching a group of eight WPA artists who were associated with the New York City Federal Art Poster Projects in 1938-1939. One of these artists was Harry Herzog." The woman who sent the letter went on to explain, "As I puzzle through this research I am not sure if I have made the right connections." She ended with, "My hope is that it will be agreeable to you that we might speak or communicate by email." When we eventually talked on the phone, I learned that the Calendar Eight, as she nicknamed them, were artists who designed the prints for the WPA calendar published in 1939. With her meticulous eye for detail, the researcher had noticed that the dates in that year corresponded exactly with those of 2017. As a board member of the National New Deal Preservation Association, she had the calendar reprinted and reissued with a different year on the cover. My father designed the picture for January.

After my parents' divorce in the mid 1940s, I lived with my mother in a small apartment. It was a walkup in a brownstone in Manhattan's Murray Hill neighborhood. Occasionally, my father came to see me. From my early memories, I only ever recall him saying one thing to me. On an evening when he visited, my father made up a shaggy dog story in order to get me to go to sleep. "This dog walks into a bar and…" I must have drifted off not understanding at all what any mangy animal would be doing in a place where adults went to drink.

Another time when he was at the apartment, I had just completed a watercolor self-portrait. The face on the stick figure portrayed my asymmetrical smile. Each twig-like arm sprouted three straggly fingers. The entire fragile body tilted as if a storm were blowing furiously across the page. "Daddy, daddy, paint a picture for me," I pleaded. Without hesitating, my father picked up the child-sized brush and within minutes he produced the unequivocal likeness of a cow.

Somewhere along the labyrinthine twists and turns of my life, I lost those two pictures. But one of them still exists and, most likely, always will. The cow stands in a pastoral field of grass and cotton candy pink flowers. In the sky above float poodle white clouds. It is an ideal summer's day. My father created this picture to publicize a five-borough outdoor exhibition of children's art. When I first came upon the poster in a book, I thought back to that evening in New York and the cow my father painted for me. Was the picture arbitrary? Or, as I hoped, was there a link between that complacent animal looking out through circles of wide, wondering eyes and my father's paternal instinct that manifested itself a few years later?

"It costs nineteen dollars and thirty-nine cents," the researcher responded to my enquiry about purchasing a copy of the calendar. I hesitated at this unorthodox amount. She continued with a smirk in her voice, "The price is the same as the year when it was originally published." I ordered the calendar.

When I received the ordinary brown cardboard box, I didn't know what to expect. Suppose it was of no consequence? Suppose it was just like other calendars with images that get replaced each month throughout the year the way we change what we wear with the weather and with each new color, style or fad. I was relieved when I opened the package and found just what I hoped it would be. Something remarkable.

Here with me now, it is like a newborn child to be marveled at for its sweetness, innocence and the indisputable fact that it is solely mine. It isn't in an oversized book or an impersonal government building for everyone to see. Mine. I treat it accordingly, viewing it only at particular moments. I am determined to preserve its newness and do not want to disturb its peaceful rest.

The calendar remains in the box. Why do I keep it there? Possibly to preserve its uniqueness. I am protecting it and keeping it safe from harm. I don't yet know where to hang it. I want to parade it around and show other people. I want to testify to them "Look, this is what my father created. He did exist. He was someone special." Here is the undeniable confirmation of the existence of a bond between my father and me.

Eventually, I will hang the calendar on the wall. It will forever be turned to January. The page's forget-me-not blue background reminds me of the sky in the poster of the cow. But the clouds in *this* scene are gray. The town, with its church and brown-roofed houses, pauses under constantly falling snow. Three reindeer stand alert facing out towards the forest, their antlers echoing the bare tree branches curved in arcs by bracing wind. It is an ideal winter's day.

Bethel, Connecticut, 1969

It was late August, 1969. The glow from the Summer of Love still lingered. The Vietnam War continued on a far off continent. I was visiting my mother in her white with blue trim, clapboard country house in Connecticut. Without warning, the telephone's harsh notes interrupted the flawless afternoon. My mother picked up the receiver. After a brief conversation, she put it back in its cradle and turned to me. "Your father has died," she told me softly.

This calamitous moment was not the anticipated but dreaded call from the hospital. Not the polite knock on the door from the police. Instead, a meteor from outer space crashed into the earth. It was an anomaly. It had nothing to do with my young adulthood.

And everything to do with it.

When I was six, my father completely disappeared from my life. My mother, of sturdy English stock, persevered with a stiff upper lip. We never talked about my father. We soldiered through. Or, at least, she did. I cried for him every night. I didn't really care about presents at Christmas and on my birthday. I just wanted my father to return home. Now he had left for good with no hope of a letter or phone call or just showing up.

Without telling anyone, my father had left New York City in the early 1950s and moved to Atlanta, Georgia. By coincidence, one of the women in his circle of friends was the mother of children with whom I had gone to elementary school. She, too, had relocated from New York to Atlanta. Although she recognized my father by his last name, she never mentioned anything to him or to us. When he died, she contacted my mother.

I didn't know what to do with my mixed emotions. The entire grief-cycle erupted in me all at once. Anger, sorrow, confusion, disappointment, and even relief competed with each other. The way a ball in a roulette wheel spins indeterminately until it stops, I had no idea where it would end up. I ran off into the woods behind the house. In a panic, my mother cried after me, "Come back! Come back! You don't have a father. You never had a father."

The next day my grandmother took the train to Connecticut from where she lived in Queens. The three of us grieved in silence. We didn't share any fond memories. We didn't stare nostalgically at grayed-out pictures. We didn't exchange reminiscences. We didn't outwardly show any remorse or regret.

I talked to the woman in Atlanta again a few days later and received more information. When my father moved there he joined the peace and social justice movement. As an artist, he designed and printed signs for protests and marches. While opposed to the Vietnam conflict, he remained a proud World War II veteran. For that reason, when my father died his friends buried him in the veteran's cemetery in Marietta, Georgia. On top of his grave they appropriately placed a peace symbol made of white flowers.

I was invited to my father's memorial service in Atlanta that September. "You don't want to go, do you?" my mother asked. It was more of an entreaty than a question. It would be a betrayal to her, a slap in the face. She had stood by me and been the sole parent. She had done so much to try to make up for my father's absence.

As I was growing up, my mother always slept in the living room so that I could have my own bedroom, a place to play with my blocks and dolls and draw and paint. She sewed some of my clothes herself. When I was a baby, my mother decorated my pinafores and overalls with delicate hand embroidery. She celebrated every event as lavishly as possible. There were tastefully wrapped, carefully selected gifts under the Christmas tree. She made sure that if my big present consisted of an envelope containing money, I also had a package to open on my birthday.

While working at a high school in downtown Manhattan, my mother prepared three meals a day in the small, narrow kitchen in our apartment. Mornings the aroma of toast lured me, albeit begrudgingly, from my warm bed. I knew there would be plenty of butter and jam to slather it with when I reached the breakfast table. Every day during high school, I carried homemade packed lunches with me. Dishes like meatloaf and macaroni and cheese frequented the table on most nights, but, there was always fresh salad with my mother's famous dressing. To this day I have no idea how she made it. The best though, was pot roast with roasted potatoes and, my favorite, lots of dark gravy, thin and savory.

In those days people didn't travel the way they do now with airplanes transporting multitudes across international boundaries on a moment by moment basis. The rich vacationed at luxury resorts or, more exotically, boarded ocean liners and headed to Europe. My mother and I usually visited friends at their summer house in New Jersey during July and August. When I was 10 years old, my mother spent the winter examining glossy travel brochures. Finally, she picked one of the candidates, probably because of its affordable prices. When school was out, my mother and I traveled for two days on a transcontinental railroad and sleeping in the Pullman car. We finally arrived at a small western town. That was the beginning of an exciting two-week adventure on a working ranch in Montana. The next year we returned for four weeks and brought one of my friends and his mother along with us.

I was now faced with the choice of attending my father's memorial service. While I didn't want to hurt my mother, a dilemma raged inside me. On the one hand, I desperately longed to go. I represented the family. This should make my attendance of special importance. I wanted to meet the people my father had known in Atlanta, and wanted them to know me. Conversely, suppose no one paid any attention to me? After all, I hadn't been part of his life while he lived there. His friends all knew each other but I was an outsider. My experience with my father had been so brief and from such a long ago time. Was I really that significant? So I didn't go to the memorial and life continued on.

Ten years passed. I traveled to the south for work and stopped off in Atlanta. I took a taxi to the Marietta cemetery. When I found my father's grave, I stood on the spot and wondered why I had come. It was just a rectangle of soil, impersonal and exactly the same as all the others in this ordered, military setting. But I stayed. I remained there for quite some time, hesitating, and making several starts and stops. Then, I began to whisper to myself. Slowly the faint skeleton of a bridge materialized. As it took shape, it arched and spanned the chasm left over from my childhood. I looked down and smiled. Finally, the search for the lost had begun.

More than Meets the Eye

Two planes hovered against a lustrous red sky. One soared in the air. The other cut through ocean waves. I stood in the post office lobby, eyes wide open, and gaped at the piece of paper in my hand. Was it true? Was it the same image that I first saw almost 30 years ago? I had just bought a sheet of stamps. The entire rectangle held 12 pictures each by a different artist. But I only saw my father's airplanes.

When I was in my 40s, an acquaintance from my childhood discovered a book on posters of the WPA. He recognized my father's name as one of the artists whose work was represented. This was how I first found out that my father had been employed as a poster artist during the Depression.

Once the book was in my possession, I searched it ravenously. To my surprise, my father's art appeared frequently throughout its pages. As I read, an insert fell out. It was a flyer for ordering enlarged reproductions of four images. One of them displayed two airplanes on a red background proudly promoting New York City's municipal airports.

Although I didn't grow up with him, I always knew that my father was an artist. Once, when I was a very little girl, I visited him in his studio apartment in New York City. I marveled at the Murphy bed that descended from the wall. In the small bathroom hung a chain I had to pull to flush the toilet. However, it was the teapot I remember most vividly. The cartoon character danced in its picture frame. Tiny legs held up a rotund body out of which shone an engaging smile. Arms and hands extended upwards lifting the brim the way a gentleman would doff a top hat to a lady. I could hear it saying "Good-day" to me.

I showed the book to my mother. While as a matter of course she never discussed my father, now she opened up a little. "Not only did your father design posters, he supervised other artists. He told them to go to museums and study the great masters." A surge of pride ran through me. For one thing, my father created many of the colorful and exquisitely executed images reproduced in this volume. He was also so well-thought of by his colleagues that they put him in charge of other artists. Then, too, he was smart, even brilliant. I always knew that. What about the time he mended my doll's eyes so that she could see again? This was just the latest affirmation of that indisputable fact. Yes, what better way to enhance one's artistic ability than to spend time in a dusty, dark place among enlightened figures? Isn't that the way all disciples learn?

I wanted more. A few years after discovering my father's connection with the WPA, I went to Washington, DC, for a conference. While there, I called the Library of Congress and was put through to the department of prints and photographs. I introduced myself to the brusque sounding librarian and explained my mission. As soon as she heard my name, she softened and inquired, "Are you related to the artist?" When I told her I was, the librarian encouraged me with, "The family would be interested in the posters of his that we have here." Since my mother had recently died and I have no siblings I replied, "*I* am the family."

On a chilly, winter day I ventured to America's national library, the largest one in the world. Once there, I asked if I could see my father's prints. I then took part in a formal ritual. After signing in, the receptionist directed me to a locked gate in a waist-high, wooden partition. Upon entering, I donned white gloves of thin, synthetic material like those used by doctors and nurses. To me, they were part of the ceremony. They should have been made of the finest silk or softest velvet and only worn on rare occasions for sacred duties. Like this one. Someone produced a portfolio of posters for me to examine. Carefully sifting through the well-protected pages, I viewed my father's art. Not small reproductions in a book, but instead, full-sized, and with the colors he originally intended. Even before I was born, my father created these gorgeous pictures. He and my mother created me. Here, at this moment, in the inner recesses of our country's archive, *we* were a family.

Afterward

Our lives are composed of strata like the earth's crust. Each band is distinguished by unique attributes that are nevertheless linked to and thereby interdependent on those layers above and below it. The way a geologist scrutinizes fragments of rocks to reconstruct the story of what evolved over the course of years and through eons of cataclysmic events, I am gradually piecing together a semblance of the man who was my father and my relationship to him.

Hedda Herzog has worked in the fields of public health and education. She is originally from New York City. She now lives in Berkeley, California, where she is launching the next phase of her life—whatever it may be.

Among Kindred Strangers

James Spence

Honorable Mention

ALICE HAD THE MILLER STRAWBERRY BLOND HAIR AND fair complexion. Summers in northwest Georgia found her barefoot, sunburned, freckled and mischievous—in Papa's estimation, the latest Miller tomboy. Only Mother's dark eyes showed the contribution of the Stephens side.

In later years, Alice would tell you that when the Great Depression fell on the family, she hardly noticed. Mother remembered differently. For her the hard times would have been easier had it never known something closer to prosperity, but it had.

With Mother's encouragement, her insistence really, Papa had worked as a brakeman on the Great Southern Railway. The family got by on his pay and what it scratched from a few acres of red clay cotton land. Every fall the children had new clothes and shoes. One especially bountiful Christmas, Alice even received a Kodak Brownie and three rolls of film along with the traditional candied dates and fresh fruit.

The Depression ended all of that along with Alice's formal education when the county shuttered its schools because there wasn't enough tax money to keep them open. Alice considered this a blessing, freeing her from numbing hours staring at ancient primers and the rote memorization that passed for schooling in those days. She was 14, had learned all she cared to know and was ready to be grown.

A few years earlier—in fact just months before the crash—Papa had paid much of the family's small savings to the Mumford Secretarial College of Atlanta for older sister Mae's tuition. At the time, he said family naturally does such things for its own and promised that everyone's turn will come.

In Atlanta, Mae boarded with Mother's sister Martha in exchange for preparing breakfast and looking after her children in the evenings. Papa had faith that after she learned shorthand, Mae would find a job and begin sending money home because that's another thing family does naturally. But even before she graduated, Mae fell captive to city ways and the ideas of her new friends. Unable to imagine herself returning to the do-without life of home, she dismissed Papa's notions as, to use the term she now applied to so many things, *démodé*.

Though he didn't really need another hand, Mother's uncle Moody Stephens hired older brother Bill at the sawmill. There he fell in with the roughest of the loggers, learned to gamble and commenced his life-long devotion to white liquor. On his sixteenth birthday, younger brother Henry signed on with the WPA. Defying Mother and Papa, he married Frances Jackson and moved in with her parents. Their baby is due not long after the New Year.

Only three remained at home.

When Henry married and moved down the road, the family's nightly card games ended. Now they sat silent until bedtime, Papa with eyes closed and hands folded over his chest, while the women patched, darned or did handwork by the dim coal oil glow.

Alice found a job with Mr. John Pickett at his spread house. For $18 a week, she worked 12-hour days Monday through Saturday tying fringe onto chenille bedspreads—the pastel ones seen flapping in the breeze for sale alongside every roadway. With her wages, the family bought sugar, corn meal, flour, lard, salt and the coal oil. That and vegetables, fresh from the garden in the summertime and preserved during the rest of the year, the annual hog, eggs from the chickens and milk from the cow provided them enough to eat. For most everything else, until Papa could find work they relied on help from Mother's sisters, themselves only a little better off than the family.

The difference was that their husbands, timid men who settled for less than a brakeman's higher wages and dangerous duties during the good times, managed to hold onto their jobs during the bad.

The cost of this familial charity was Mother's profound humiliation. As a girl she had been the star of her family, her father's favorite and the one of them all thought destined to marry well. She faulted Papa, not the times or the railroad, and certainly not herself, for the failure of her fate.

One day the mailman stopped for more than to share the community gossip and enjoy a gourd of well water. He handed Mother an envelope and said, "It's for John from Enid, Oklahoma. From a lawyer it appears."

From the front porch swing Papa said, "I don't have my glasses. Read it, Mother."

Holding the envelope unopened and at arm's length she replied, "I won't. It omens bad news and I'll not be the one to announce it."

"I know it's from Oklahoma and it's from a lawyer, but it's already written and the words aren't going to change because you're the one reading them. I'd appreciate if you would read it."

Thus inoculated, she read what they both suspected the letter would report:

> *November 3, 1932*
>
> *Dear Mr. Miller:*
> *I am saddened to inform you of the passing of your father, Thomas J. Miller on October 15 at about 7:20 P.M. At the time he lodged at the Shawnee Hotel here in Enid. He had finished his evening meal and was walking up the stairs to his room when seized of a heart attack. He died then and there, not suffering unduly.*
>
> *Your brother Monroe and sister Ruth arranged for a fine Christian burial that was attended by all of his other children who was able to get here and many townspeople.*
>
> *Mr. Miller left a Will dividing his belongings among all his children. He named you and Monroe as the*

oldest boys of each set of his children in charge of the estate. After settling his debts, the share for each son will be about $1,950 and $975 for each daughter.

At the visitation Monroe told me that Mr. Miller spoke of you often, including the week before his death when he visited Monroe's ranch. He expressed hope that you were prospering in these hard times, saying you deserved to, and gave you much credit for the success of many of your brothers and sisters out here.

I am sorry that I must ask you to come to Enid as soon as you can, but under Oklahoma law before you can act as Executor you must take the oath in person before our local Probate Judge. On the same day you can sign the papers to get your money as Monroe has already collected up the assets, sold what needed to be sold and paid the debts.

Monroe can advance money for the trip from your share if need be. Just let me know.

Awaiting your earliest reply, I am,
Sincerely,

Hal Washburn
Attorney at Law

Mother handed the letter to Papa, who sat silent until after the mailman extended condolences and continued on his route. Then he sighed, "I always believed I'd see him one more time—I counted on it—but I won't now."

Mother said, "Imagine. At his age he had to live in a hotel all by himself. Ten children living out there and not one of them could abide him enough to take him in."

"I expect he lived in the hotel by his own choice," Papa said.

"Not with how he insisted on being waited on hand and foot for his whole life. No, if he hadn't acted like the Czar of all the Russians, he'd have died among his own instead of strangers."

When Papa chose to say nothing more, Mother could have ended the skirmish victorious as always, but it was too late for that. His defense of his father—insubordination in Mother's eyes—had caused her blood to rise. "And you of all people in this world should best know the way he was. He took you out of school in the second grade. Bound you to your Mama and then after she wore out and died to that new wife of his. It's not as if you were simple minded and wouldn't have profited from an education like he gave the rest of them. You might have amounted to something like your brothers if you'd had the chance. No sir, never any thought for you whatever. He even put you on the estate without considering you'd have to travel all the way to Oklahoma. "No, I'll never understand why you don't despise the very thought of him for what he did to you. I do."

"It was just my lot as the oldest, that's all. His brother Aaron was oldest in that family and he had the same duties as me. And I think my Papa was intending to honor my place by putting me in charge of his estate." Under Mother's increasingly icy stare he continued, "But what difference does it make anyhow? He's dead, there's no point in talking ill of him and he's treated me as well as all the rest even though we're the only ones to move so far away from him. They expect me in Oklahoma so I've got to go."

Now fully provoked by the audacity, Mother jumped to the topic always foremost in her thoughts at such a time. With one hand on her hip and the other waiving the water gourd in Papa's face for emphasis, she said, "You see John, that's the real reason you never amounted to nothin'. You let things pass too easy. No spine like me and my people. You'd better be glad I'm not goin' out there with you. I'd tell 'em what I thought of him. And I'd tell 'em what I think of all them too."

Papa said nothing more but went inside for his brakeman's denim coat and cap and a whittling knife. He came back outside, picked up a fallen branch in the sweeping yard and returned to the swing. There he sat silently whittling while keeping vigil for Alice down the road. After twilight when she finished her walk home from work, Mother met her at the front door and said, "Your Papa's Daddy has died and he'll be travelin' to Oklahoma to settle the estate. You're goin' with him to see he comes home with the money he's inherited."

"Mother, it's not my place to do that. Ain't that right, Papa?"

Before he could agree, Mother continued, "Oh yes it is your place, Alice, and you will do as I say. Somebody's got to go with Papa and I surely am not travelin' all the way to Oklahoma to be among his people again."

"But what about Mr. Pickett?"

"He can do without you for a few days. When you go to work tomorrow, just tell him. You're the best fringe tier he's got and you've never missed a day. He won't complain, but if he does tell him I said you have to go."

Two mornings later with clothing and sundries organized in neatly tied packages of brown paper and a bag of sandwiches on the back seat, Papa and Alice climbed into the Model T sedan Bill borrowed from Uncle Moody for the trip. Mother figured that if it held together, gasoline and oil would be cheaper than train passage for two, and Uncle Moody said that if it broke down it wouldn't be a great loss to bear. Just in case Mother plotted a route as close as possible to the railroad line that ran west from Rome through Birmingham, Memphis and Little Rock to Enid.

As she gave it further thought, Alice had to admit Mother was right about one thing. When Papa's in one of his moods, trances Mother calls them, he really does need someone to take care of him. He can't go to Oklahoma by himself.

When Alice accepted the inevitability of the trip, she saw that it promised a blessed change from her routine of daily fringe tying and nightly gloom. And even if Mother is right about Papa's family, still she might see a genuine Red Indian or even a cowboy. By the time the Model T sputtered to life and Mother gave final instruction to pass by all hitchhikers, Alice happily embraced the prospect of an exotic place like Oklahoma and a visit among kindred strangers. Though she had virtually no experience driving, she didn't even mind Mother's mandate to stay behind the wheel the whole way.

Papa's visage eased the minute the home place disappeared in the dust. Soon he hummed Mr. Roosevelt's tune about happy days, which he continued off and on as Alice drove out of Georgia, through Alabama and into Tennessee. After miles and hours he finally spoke, "Alice, have you ever thought about living in California? You can pick oranges right off the tree any time of year. Yes, if you had a little money in your pocket you could live right well out there. A feller might even find a job and start a whole new life if he had a mind to."

"Why, Papa! What a thing to say! You know Mother would never move to California."

"No, but we can—just you and me. There's a future out there for adventuresome spirits like ours." As Alice chuckled to herself at the absurd notion of Papa as adventuresome, he continued, "When I get my money, I was thinking we could drive straight to Los Angeles from Oklahoma and let Mother know when we get there. I'd mail some of the money to her, of course—wouldn't leave her high and dry—and I'd even send Moody enough to pay for this old automobile. That would be fair, wouldn't it? What do you say Alice?"

Without hesitation, Alice replied, "Really Papa? We're not going to do that. How could we get along without Mother?"

As she spoke, Papa saw the flash in Alice's eyes. Though he'd not seen it in her before he knew it and he understood it. Suddenly chilled, he reached to the back seat for a blanket. As he wrapped himself in it he again fell silent, eyes closed and hands folded over his chest. He would ride that way to Enid and then all the way home, cocooned in his fantasy of a California life.

At least, he thought, *no one can take that away from me.*

James Spence is 70 years old and still working as a practicing lawyer in Decatur, GA.

The White Blouse

BRENDA GUYTON
Recognized

WHEN I WAS GROWING UP IN WEST TEXAS IN THE 1950S, life was slow and boring. I was an only child, a tomboy, with a voracious reading habit and a burning desire to know about all living creatures (except humans). When stuck indoors, I read all about animals. Later in high school, one of my English teachers threw up her hands and said, "Why are all your book reports about animal books? Don't you read anything else?"

There were lots of sunny days in the desert which allowed me to spend most of my free time digging in the vacant lot two doors down the alley from my house. Since this was in a desert town of West Texas, the lot consisted of sand, rock hard sand-colored dirt, and scrubby weeds.

And delightful critters.

There were a handful of long, sleek, green lizards - magical lizards whose tails grew back when the tips were bitten off by the not-quite-fast-enough neighborhood tom cat.

There were a few hardy bugs living in our area, mostly beetle types that were crunchy treats for the lizards. Thanks to my many, many, many hours (years really) of patient watching, I was able to see the occasional life/death drama as fascinating to me as any human drama could be. For instance, one day I was perched on a branch in the small tree in our back yard watching the webworms moving around in their circular webby home. I watched them and wondered about their life cycles, mating rituals, etc.

Suddenly, a black and red wasp landed on the side of the web. The wasp stuck his head through the web, poked a long proboscis into the nearest worm, and instantly sucked him dry. Only the shrunken husk of his wrinkled skin was left. Then he went to the next worm, and the next one – like a hungry cowboy at an all-you-can-eat buffet. How cool is that?

There were also the peculiarly flat disk-shaped horned lizards who ate only red ants. The lizards were known locally as horny toads. (I know. There is a certain connotation to that word now, but not in that time and place.)

I had read about this lizard's ancient and peculiar defense mechanism but had never seen it in action, even though I captured and released many of them.

They are tiny dinosaurs about four inches long and outfitted with full armor. Short spikes cover their backs, and they sport two long horns on their heads. Their leathery backs display a desert camouflage of light and dark brownish spots.

They also have spots on their flat, scaly stomachs. Some kid at school told me the number of spots represented how many ants they had eaten. As an adult, I now laugh at my naiveté, but at the time I took his claims under consideration and started counting the spots on the toads that I caught (and released). Of course, it turned out to be a false hypothesis.

One Sunday morning, when I was about eight years old, my parents decided to go out to eat after church. This was unprecedented. My father was a diesel mechanic and my mother a stay-at-home mom, so money was tight. I couldn't remember when we had ever eaten out. It suddenly made sense to me why I was outfitted in a brand-new frilly white cotton blouse that my mother washed and ironed.

She hated ironing. She had to wash and iron my dad's uniforms every week and complained about it bitterly each and every time. (This was prior to the time when we got a washing machine, so she had to wash everything by hand.) Clearly, this blouse and this excursion were important enough to her to spend the money on a blouse that would not be worn to school, and also to overcome her aversion to ironing.

After church, we stopped back at the house for something before going on to the restaurant. Mom said they were going to be a few minutes, so I asked (begged actually) to go to the vacant lot.

My mother put her hand on my shoulder and attempted to impress upon me what a big deal the cost of the new blouse was, and also how long it took her to carefully iron each of the three rows of many stiff frills that ran down the front of the blouse from neck to waist.

I stood patiently and waited. She rolled her eyes, and said I had to be back in 10 minutes and to NOT GET DIRTY!!

As always, I approached the lot slowly to avoid scaring any critters. They would dart into their hidey holes at the first sight of sudden movement. Then I saw him. The largest horny toad ever! Much bigger than the palm of my hand. A truly gorgeous creature with an almost artistic design of spots and stripes on his back. Impressively sharp burnished horns. A primeval glower designed to strike fear into any lurking predator.

And I caught him! I was so excited !!!

This achievement could not be overstated. I captured the granddaddy of all horny toads.

He was magnificent. More than that, he was regal in his disdain for me. He was totally unafraid and glared at me with those steely black eyes—clearly commanding me to release him. I promised him I would, but first I had to show off my prize. I started running. I couldn't wait to show Mr. Amazing to my parents.

When I got home, I stopped just outside the screen door.

This requires an aside: I was no longer allowed to take any creature into the house after the unfortunate spider incident. One evening I captured a beautiful black fuzzy spider with white spots. I put him in a jar with some twigs and leaves and covered it with wax paper held by a rubber band. I poked small holes in the wax paper so he could breathe. My plan was to set the jar on my bedside nightstand and observe his movements until I fell asleep, then to release him in the morning.

He turned out to be a she. When I woke up, there were zillions of impossibly teensy black and white spiders crawling on the nightstand, on my bed, on the floor, and pretty much everywhere. I was delighted to discover that spiders could be so tiny. I eventually managed to catch and release all of them, but my mother was beyond horrified, and that circumstance resulted in the banishment of all critters from the house forevermore.

Back to our story:

I yelled through the screen door to my parents to come see my prize. My mother came to the door but didn't open it. She peered through the screen to acknowledge my achievement. (This was our routine now since I couldn't take the animals into the house.)

I held up the magnificent creature and struck a pose holding him in front of me. I wished we had a camera to capture my triumph. I was as proud as any zoologist would be with a new discovery.

At that moment, my large and angry lizard let me know just how agitated he was by triggering his extraordinary defense mechanism—he squirted a long stream of bright red blood from his eyes that hit the ruffles on my white blouse from chest to waistline.

I was thrilled!! I had long dreamed of seeing this ancient prehistoric action that I had read so much about.

My mother screamed.

Brenda Guyton spent her working years as a financial director. Now retired, she indulges in creative pursuits that include painting and writing. Her paintings can be seen on her website. Her writing is usually well hidden. She lives in Dallas with her husband and her three Maine Coon cats.

All That Matters

PENNY MICHALSKI

Recognized

Here I am
At the end
With all that matters.

A latchkey kid who'd face down the strap
If supper wasn't cooking
If the water for coffee wasn't boiling
As she walked through the door
If the dishes weren't done
If homework wasn't done
If the neighbors found out.

She has heart palpitations
Mother would tell the doctor.
Such a nervous child
He'd say,
Oblivious of his complicity.

Children of immigrants
Whose only desire was to be free,

To live as they pleased
Were now empowered to
Echo the cruelty of the life left behind
To their kitchens and bedrooms.

The lesson was not to become them
But to stay a paper doll
That bends to authority
Of teachers
Of bosses
Of spouses
Kept unaware of her own beating heart.

But when they came to their end
All that mattered
Was still with them
Making supper
Making coffee
Wiping a chin
The neighbors always knew.

Penny Michalski is presently in her last creative writing class at Stanford, editing her upcoming novel, *How Witches Fly.* In the meantime, she's had poetry published in *Red River Review, Three Line Poetry Issue 45* and most recently in *Poetry Quarterly* (Fall 2017). Her flash fiction has appeared in *Paragraph Planet* four times.

SPECIAL POETRY PRIZE

The Door Gunner

J. Allen Whitt,

Special Poetry Prize

As tropic dawn inflamed the east,
The sky forewarned of blood.
Montana Kid was standing down,
But Hipshot had to fly.

They met for breakfast in the mess,
And over coffee there,
Amid the silence Hipshot said,
"I won't come back today."

The Kid just gave a hollow laugh.
"Don't joke around like that."
"I dreamed my boots were empty, Kid.
The sign was really clear."

The Kid said, "Aw, don't worry none.
A dream don't mean a thing."
But Hipshot shook his head and said,
"I know my time is up."

When Hipshot moved his chair to go,
The Kid held out his hand.
"I'll take your place out there today."
But Hipshot shook his head.

"No, Kid, the duty's mine today.
I've never missed a flight."
With that, he gathered up his gear
And headed for the line.

The crew chief made a final check,
Then yelled, "Let's turn and burn!"
The turbine whined, the rotors flashed,
As they lifted from the pad.

The Huey topped a hazy ridge,
And Hipshot cocked his gun,
But watching from the jungle below,
A sniper sighted in.

Its windshield stitched with bullet holes,
The Huey returned to base.
There Hipshot lay among curettes,
Without a tongue or jaw.

When medics brought the body bag,
The Kid requested time.
His fingers closed his buddy's eyes.
His hands zipped up the bag.

The Kid heals slow among the pines,
While fifty years slip by.
Now hands tie Copper Johns and nymphs,
Beneath Montana sky.

Yet sometimes eyes that will not shut
Stare through the shroud of night,
And solace lies beyond the stars,
'til dawn restores the light.

J. Allen Whitt is a Vietnam veteran of three combat deployments to the Gulf of Tonkin aboard an aircraft carrier. He recently retired as a Professor Emeritus of Sociology. His novel *Notes From the Other Side of the Mountain: Love Confronts the Wounds of War,* was a finalist in the 2013 New Mexico-Arizona Book Awards. An essay of his won first place in a national creative writing contest for veterans. He has publications in *Military Experience and the Arts, Fifty-Something, Lyric, Cream City Review, Lowestoft Chronicle, Good Old Days, Reminisce, Front Porch, Westview, Concho Review,* and *Louisville Magazine.*

JUDGING TEAM

Judging Team Members

August 1, 2019

THE HEART AND SOUL OF AGELESS AUTHORS IS AN OUTstanding cadre of judges, volunteers who are generous with their time and expertise. They lend critical thought to our effort and we could not conduct our writing contests or populate our anthologies without them. They are mostly writers, editors, educators, and professional people who reside all over the world. We are in awe of their talent and their keen understanding of the written word.

Many of our judges have reviewed submissions in more than one contest over the last few years. The following is a list of our judges as of August 1, 2019.

Team Leaders

Jane Giddan, Carrollton, Texas

Ann Howells, Carrollton, Texas

John Tuttle, Cherry Valley, Illinois

Team Members

Samuel Cole, Woodbury, Minnesota
Amanda Warren, Aiken, South Carolina
Laura McCullough, Ellijay, Georgia
Leah Chaffins, Lawton, Oklahoma
Deborah LeFalle, San Jose, California
Alice Mathews, Carrollton, Texas
James Hanlon, Rochester Hills, Michigan
Pamela Vass, Looe, Cornwall, United Kingdom
Edith S. Cook, Wheatland, Wyoming
Pam Palmer, Frisco, Texas
Jake Sauls, Wichita Falls, Texas
Stephanie Massicote, Orangeville, Ontario, Canada
Lanie Goodell, Aurora, Colorado
Ali Flake, Waldorf, Maryland
William French, Mentor, Ohio
Mini Gautam, Bidhan Nagar, Kolkata India
Lynn Baker, Dallas, Texas
Julie Hogg, Dallas, Texas
Mari Escobar, Dallas, Texas
Joyce Brinkman, Zionsville, Indiana
Adam Levon Brown, Eugene, Oregon
Candice Kelsey, Los Angeles, California
Margaret Abrusley, Dallas, Texas
Gwen Mintz, Las Cruces, New Mexico
Eric Scholz, Fair Lawn, New Jersey
Juliana Filisanu, Ontigola, Toledo, Castilla-La Mancha, Spain
Alexej Savreux, Mission, Kansas
Cheryl Nugent, Orangeburg, South Carolina
Laura Austin, Beaver Dam, Kentucky
Laura Roberts, Sacramento, California
Judy Irwin, Mabank, Texas
Morgan Christie, Winston Salem, North Carolina
Shaneisha Dodson, Spring, Texas